Christians in a Technological Era

Contributors

JEAN DE LA CROIX KAELIN, O.P. Chaplain to the International
Catholic Movement for Intellectual and Cultural
Affairs of Pax Romana; chaplain to Catholic stu-
dents at the University of Geneva.

JEAN LADRIÈRE. Professor in the Faculty of Philosophy, Catholic University of Louvain, Belgium.

MARGARET MEAD. Curator of Ethnology, The American
Museum of Natural History; past president of
American Anthropological Association, member
of United States delegation to the United Nations
Conference on the Application of Science and
Technology for the Benefit of the Less Developed
Areas; member Commission on Church and So-
ciety, World Council of Churches.

BERNARD MOREL. Professor in Theological Faculty, University
of Geneva; pastor of Cathédrale de St. Pierre,
Geneva.

SCOTT I. PARADISE. Associate Director, Detroit Industrial Mission. Formerly on the staff of Sheffield Industrial
Mission, Sheffield, England.

MICHAEL POLANYI. Professor of Philosophy, Merton College,
Oxford, England.

FRANÇOIS RUSSO, S.J. Director, Economic Research Center, In-
stitute of Applied Economic Sciences; member of
National Centre for Scientific Research; ecclesias-
tic adviser to International Catholic Centre for
Co-ordination with UNESCO; chaplain to Catholic
Union of Scientists and to International Secreta-
riat of Pax Romana.

HUGH C. WHITE, JR. Executive Director, Detroit Industrial
Mission.

Christians
in a
Technological Era

HUGH C. WHITE, JR.,
Editor

MARGARET MEAD

MICHAEL POLANYI

JEAN LADRIÈRE

BERNARD MOREL

FRANÇOIS RUSSO, S.J.

JEAN DE LA CROIX KAELIN, O.P.

SCOTT I. PARADISE

NEW YORK
1964

Acknowledgments

The Publisher gratefully acknowledges the permission granted by M. Valdo Galland, Secretary of the World Student Christian Federation, Geneva, to reprint the papers of Michael Polanyi, Jean Ladrière, Bernard Morel, François Russo, S.J., and Jean de la Croix Kaelin, O.P., which appear in this book. These papers were first delivered at a Consultation held at Louvain, Belgium, April 1961, under the sponsorship of the World Student Christian Federation and Pax Romana, "an international Catholic movement for intellectual and cultural affairs." The papers were first published in *The Student World*, LIV: 3 (1961). The translations from French were made by Margaret House.

Editor's Preface

This book deserves careful reading and discussion by adults concerned for the immediate future of Christian thought in America. The subject of the book, "Christians in a Technological Era," is the preoccupation of every churchman whether he recognizes it or not.

A familiar question is, "What are you doing?" We are a nation of doers, activists—technicians on a large or small scale. Personal identity is in terms of being a salesman, stenographer, designer, engineer, trainer, lab technician, assembler, inspector, copy writer, draftsman, economist, or clergyman. In the home the housewife or husband, "man about the house," is described and evaluated in terms of skills. "Mary is an excellent cook, but she can't make the baby's formula." "John is a good engineer, but he can't handle the family checkbook." Nothing is more highly valued in America than skilled technique. This is the technological era.

Curiously and tragically the Church in America has turned its back on the development of technology. At the end of the nineteenth century and the first quarter of this century there were heated debates on the subject of science and religion, evolution, and the validity of the inspired word of God. But since the great depression in the thirties the churches have been more and more on the sidelines, disengaged from the mainstream of American

thought, occupied with private life, commonly referred to as pastoral care.

This book moves beyond the analysis-paralysis of
so many theological and sociological studies of
Christian thought in our day, and faces squarely
the crucial question of what Christianity means
and does not mean in the midst of racing technology. The subject is attacked from quite different
positions by both theologians and scientists. The
question which each chapter addresses itself to is,
"What is the relation between faith and reason in
the technician mentality today?" This question is
seriously dealt with by each of the writers.

Interestingly, each chapter of this book, exclud-
ing the first and last chapters, issued from a consultation held by the World Student Christian Federation and Pax Romana in Louvain, Belgium, in
1961. The introductory chapter by the distinguished American anthropologist Margaret Mead
cogently interprets the book's theme for the American scene, and the concluding chapter by an experienced practitioner, Scott I. Paradise, recommends
in realistic terms a strategy for extending the
dialogue.

In most recent years the churches, synagogues,
and temples in America have been awakened to the
challenge of urbanization but continue to neglect
the basic issue of technology. The material in this
book is timely for it offers an opportunity for an
ecumenical dialogue between Roman Catholic,
Orthodox, Protestant and Anglican churchmen
(and non-churchmen) on a pertinent church-in-
the-world theme.

HUGH C. WHITE, JR.

Contents

Christians in a Technological Era

Introduction

THIS book is directed toward those who take religion seriously—those who cannot conceive of a life bearing a religious label which is not infused with that religion. At the present time such people are at a disadvantage in the United States. It is reluctantly recognized that there are those whose lives center on religion: the clergy (who should not overemphasize the religious aspect of their career), monks and nuns (who seem increasingly out of place in the contemporary American world), some Roman Catholics (especially those belonging to certain self-conscious ethnic groups), various separatist sects (whose members confine their lives within the framework of beliefs that hold them together and separate them from the world), and the occasional individual who, as the French would say, is *un person croyant et pieux*. But most Americans—even though they acknowledge some slight connection with religion, accept the label of some denomination, and obey a certain set of ritualistic requirements—do not admit the existence of a significant connection between the lives they lead, the careers they pursue, the thoughts they think, and their relationship to God or their spiritual existence.

In this atmosphere, the old battles between science and religion—once exemplified in the sturdy atheism of the country editor—are dying away. It is difficult even to obtain a statement of the issues. Most young Americans tend to find absurd any attempt to juxtapose the historic Christian doctrine and our cybernetic age. And for those few who have embraced a religious vocation with enthusiasm, the idea of facing the modern scientific revolution is almost unthinkable; in making their vocational choice they are likely to ignore anything that has been said or thought in the last two hundred years.

For such individuals, it is perfectly acceptable to disapprove of television, worry mildly about the unemployment of youth, frown over the increase in juvenile delinquency, lament the decay of morals, criticize "Madison Avenue" (while increasingly adopting Madison Avenue tactics), and denounce subliminal advertising or a book like *Tropic of Cancer*. But it is a different matter altogether to consider seriously the position of the Christian to whom Christianity is a way of life in a world in which men have the power to destroy all human life —to destroy, in fact, all life—and the power to give abundant life to all human beings, powers which once were believed to belong only to God.

It is one of the merits of the ecumenical movement that it endows with new life certain older ways of living and thinking which had become stale and complacent. Furthermore, it is a means of breaking down the barriers of isolation, specialization, and compensatory hostility. In the past, the different emphases developed within each particular area of isolation deepened some perceptions while neglecting others. These several insights are now made available to the whole Christian community, and the spirit is uplifted as more of mankind is encompassed in a widened embrace.

So this ecumenical debate—the fundamental premises of which are essentially unfamiliar to most Americans, who are busy with good works and are sustained by unexamined faith—should cut through to the very core of our indifference. The five European discussants are primarily concerned with intellectual issues but their arguments, considered seriously, should also have meaning for the Christian position on such matters as racial integration, the measures necessary to create a warless world, the responsibility of one generation to the next in ensuring that no irreversible damage is done to soil or air or water, to fish or bird or forest, and the willingness of man to accept a burden perhaps even greater than that laid on humanity when our primal parents first ate of the fruit of the tree of knowledge of good and evil—the burden of responsibility for the survival of life on earth.

At the heart of the discussion is the question of the place of the world in the life and the solicitude of the Christian and the scriptural grounds for cherishing or rejecting it. In Christian history, the world, the flesh, and the devil have been variously defined, and one of the problems of our era is a reclarification of their interrelationship. Christ said: "My kingdom is not of this world." Should Christians, therefore, ignore the world? Should they accept the position taken by some clergymen, whom I have heard say, in effect: "Well, you scientists made the bomb. It's up to you to deal with it"? Or the even more fundamentalist position: "This world is filled with sin and iniquity, and the sooner it is destroyed the better"? Should Christians take the position that it is the function of this world to "colonize heaven"—and does this mean that the world should be decently run? Are the principalities and the powers not only secular but also essentially profane and the object of Christian avoidance? Or have Christians a responsibility when the law courts mete out a different kind of justice to the rich and to the poor?

And the flesh? For two thousand years Christians, as individuals, have taken to heart the injunction, "Feed the hungry," and have given to the needy in various forms of charity. But because scientific knowledge and the supporting technology were lacking, millions died in famines and epidemics. Even today, most Christians find more vivid and appealing the image of the soup kitchen for the victims of poverty or earthquakes or floods or war than they do the plans made by the World Health Organization for the prevention of epidemics or by the Food and Agriculture Organization for an adequate world food supply. Christian compassion, on the part of the fortunate, and Christian resignation, on the part of victims of tribulation, still prevail as the true expressions of Christian giving. And many see no inconsistency between their belief in giving and their abhorrence of "socialized medicine," "foreign aid," government sponsored programs of flood control, or international campaigns to eradicate malaria. This was the issue, more than any other, that led the converted natives of the Admiralty Islands to break away from their missionaries. "They told us the truth," the converts said. "But they did not show us the way." [1]

And it is on these questions—the stewardship of the earth, the cultivation of the earth as a garden, and the command to feed and heal all men—that the issue is joined. In earlier times, the Christian, intent on his own soul and the life of the world to come, might devote himself to giving alms, rescuing orphans, and comforting the dying. These relationships provided a satisfactory dynamic tension within which donor and recipient benefited spiritually. But in the present era the conception of giving must be revised. Is it Christian to insist that it is nobler to minister to the individual sufferer than to use technology to wipe out the disease from which that individual is suffering?

The reverberations of this necessary change in relationship between donor and recipient go far beyond the mere reorganization of local charity or the acceptance of measures of social security essential in our technological era. They ring through the new declaration of the 3rd Lambeth Conference:[2]

"Our unity in Christ, expressed in our full communion, is the most profound bond among us, in

[1] Margaret Mead, *New Lives for Old: Cultural Transformation—Manus, 1928-1953* (New York: William Morrow & Co., Inc., 1956).

[2] See *A Statement from the Primates and Metropolitans of the Anglican Communion* in *Anglican Congress 1963* (New York: Seabury Press, 1963), p. 118.

all our political and racial and cultural diversity.

"The time has fully come when this unity and interdependence must find a completely new level of expression and corporate obedience.

"Our need is not, therefore, simply to be expressed in greater generosity by those who have money and men to spare. Our need is rather to understand how God has led us, through the sometimes painful history of our time, to see the gifts of freedom and communion in their great terms, and to live up to them. If we are not responsible stewards of what Christ has given us, we will lose even what we have."

The technological capabilities of the modern world have bound together all men, one species in one community, and this new interdependence is creating a climate of opinion in which the older dependence of the have-nots on the benevolence of the haves is being replaced by a new idea of partnership in the use of technology. In international organizations the older societies, which at present have the greatest technical resources, and the newer societies, which need these resources, can work together as partners of equal dignity, members one of another.

Just as in the latter days of Rome the new Christian ethic produced a new technical application when, for the first time, hospitals were established to care for the poor, so today the new technology demands a new ethical application. Yet perhaps at no other time has the gap been so great between the explicit tenets of Christianity and the attempt to utilize in the service of Christian principles the possibilities offered by existing technology. Christian institutions continue to follow an inappropriate, inadequate, and no longer relevant style of individual Christian charity; in doing so, they surrender to the secular world—even the Communist world —the wider goals of feeding the hungry, caring for the sick, and protecting the poor in ways that can lead to the abolition of hunger, chronic illness, and poverty.

The question of whether technology as a whole is to be placed on the side of good or evil is the third of the set of perennial problems with which these discussants are concerned. For Americans, the European emphasis may seem strange, since even those Americans who feel that science may be evil seldom doubt that technology is good. Obdurant and recalcitrant as some Americans are in their attitudes toward Darwinian theory or contemporary astronomical theories of the origins of the universe, they enthusiastically accept almost every technological achievement—the automobile, the airplane, radio, television, refrigeration and air conditioning, plastics and other synthetic materials —and they pause only briefly over the man-made satellite because they do not yet see its usefulness or because the Russians put one into orbit first. The European's deep distrust of the machine, which seems to him to be destroying the "human scale" and man's classic humanity, is very slightly developed in the United States and is seldom encountered here except in the cloistered halls devoted to the humanities. Consequently, this part of the argument will perhaps be mystifying to Americans.

They may well ponder and need to investigate further Kaelin's statement (p. 125) that "the Christian must face the real risks which technology causes him to run," for Kaelin is referring to spiritual risks, not (as one might easily assume) the risk of the obliteration of the human race.

However, in spite of the generally acceptant American attitude toward machines—which English Luddites once tried to destroy as the destroyers of their handicraft livelihood—American Christians are in some danger of turning against the new cybernetic machines. Lacking any depth of thinking about the modern world, they may well regard the whole idea of computers and automation as essentially evil and demonic ways of dehumanizing man. Morel's lucid discussion of the scientific basis of automation and of the way in which information theory can be integrated into theology touches the very heart of this issue. He views cybernetics as a new way of describing the organization of the universe, as part of the grand design, and as descriptive of a process going on perhaps even in inanimate matter. Viewed in this way, the cybernetic revolution is not a set of mathematical principles which, in effect, reduce human beings to ciphers in the service of large, power-thirsty aggregations of nuts and bolts. Instead, it is a great leap forward in man's humanity, comparable to other revolutionary advances—man's recognition that tools can be fashioned, that animals can be bred and that seeds can be planted, that the seasons recur, that spoken language can be reduced to written form, that fire need not be feared as an enemy but, domesticated, can be welcomed as a source of safety and comfort.

Christianity happily accepted all these earlier triumphs of man's increasing knowledge of nature —the seed, the plow and the reaper's scythe, the husbandman with his flock, the hearth, the script which made possible the scriptures. But, it should be noted, these insights, through which man vastly improved the efficiency of his stewardship and increased the extent of his dominion over the earth, came before the Old Testament was written and were firmly incorporated into civilization long before the coming of Christ. And Christianity, which blesses the time-honored forms through which man exercises his intelligence and systematizes his knowledge of nature, shows only a limited capacity to accept new insights and to bless new forms.

Today, as in the past, resistance to new forms of knowledge has its source both in accepted practice and in a general psychological resistance to change in modes of thinking. Automation threatens established interests, such as those of trade unionists— and this at a time when, belatedly, some Christians are learning to appreciate the need for trade unionism. But the greatest immediate challenge is to our mode of thinking about scarcity and plenty: From a central concern with the problem of how to provide a paying job for everyone so that production can be kept up, we must shift to a concern with the problem of how to provide a basis of intelligent consumption for everyone so that our incredible productive capacity can be used. This challenge will have to be met first in the United States, and there is little in traditional American Protestant thought which prepares us to meet it.[3]

The discussions of science in this volume deal with problems which are equally urgent and perhaps of even greater interest. The primary emphasis here is on science as an approach to knowledge which has much in common with other approaches to an understanding of the universe. The twentieth century conception of science as a continuing search is a welcome contrast to the earlier static and absolutist conception with its ineluctable conclusion that if science is right, then religion must be wrong. (That this viewpoint still has its adherents is evident in many contemporary discussions of the teaching of evolution.[4]) Absolute revelation, however parochial the interpretation of the vision and archaic the language, confronted absolute truth and this arrogant, exclusive absolutism —shared by scientists and religious thinkers alike —resulted in a stalemate which still paralyzes the thinking of some living scientists and theologians. Phrased in this way, no synthesis—indeed no search for synthesis—was possible.

Beginning with a different phrasing, Polanyi, in his illuminating discussion of the I-Thou dimension and the I-Me dimension as well as the I-It

[3] See, for example, Donald N. Michael, *Cybernetics: The Silent Conquest* (Santa Barbara, California: Center for the Study of Democratic Institutions, 1962), and Robert Theobald, *Free Men and Free Markets* (New York: Clarkson N. Potter, Inc., 1963).

[4] See, for example, Russell L. Mixter, ed., *Evolution and Christian Thought Today* (Grand Rapids, Michigan: Wm. B. Eerdmans Publishing Co., 1959).

dimension developed by the physical sciences, in his lucid statement of the commonality of approach in religion and science, and in his conception of comprehension, moves toward synthesis and transcends older, stiff attempts to work out such a synthesis.

So also Russo's description of scientific method should reassure the humanist even as it delights the mind of the scientist. Particularly important is his recognition of a relatively new aspect of our contemporary pursuit of truth (pp. 96, 98):

"Science as we know it today appears to be increasingly based on a *love of research*. By this we mean that the ideal of the scientist today is not so much the attainment and contemplation of truth as progress towards it, the strain of the whole being to achieve it. . . . At this point science no longer appears as a minor or optional form of occupation on a par with a number of others. It appears as a *vital* activity which man cannot do without, any more than he can do without bread. It constitutes a task in which man possesses himself, frees himself, and knows himself, for the reason that we have just given, that it is his deepest vocation."

But science does not only give us new ways of comprehending the universe and new sources of self-knowledge. Science also, in its application, gives us new ways of meeting our Christian obligations. The sciences of chemistry, biology, and nutrition have given us new ways of obeying the injunction, "Feed my lambs." The development of medicine, epidemiology, virology, and bacteriology

has given us new ways to "heal the sick." New concepts of social organization and knowledge of how
society functions open to us new ways in which man
can "seek first the Kingdom of God and His right-
eousness." And our study of the minds of children
is revealing the existence of a human need which is
as deep as hunger and thirst, as compelling as the
need for rest and the need for love—that is, a need
to relate to the universe, a "cosmic sense,"[5]
through which religion has grown and continually
becomes meaningful to man.

There are, however, two points at which, it seems
to me, the writers of these essays, with all their
luminous modernity and sensitivity, have stopped
short of facing major issues. First, there is the problem of justifying involvement in the technological
improvement of man's lot through the biblical
command giving man "dominion . . . over every
living thing that moveth upon the earth" (Gen.
1:28). The idea of *dominion* (as also the term *kingdom*) is obsolete in the modern world. For any definition of science as a means of giving man *dominion*—power over—tends to increase the difficulty of
realizing responsibility and of curbing exploitation.
But the definition of science as an activity leading
toward an understanding of the universe allows for
responsibility in the use of that knowledge and for
the necessity of curbing the exploitive and destruc-
tive possibilities of applied science and technology.

Secondly, these discussions, illuminated as they
are by Christian hope, fail to give adequate recogni-

[5] Edith Cobb, "The Ecology of Imagination in Childhood,"
Daedalus (Summer, 1959), pp. 537-48.

tion to the fundamental change introduced in the world by the development of nuclear, chemical, and biological weapons. Contemporary man not only has knowledge of good and evil; he has as well absolute power to destroy. This man-made power of destruction lays on man a burden he has never before experienced—a burden, like that of the knowledge of good and evil, from which he cannot escape in the foreseeable future. Given this power, the acquisition of an understanding of the natural laws which will enable men to construct, protect, and maintain a warless world is a precondition to all other benefits we may reap from our new knowledge of nature and man himself. These essays bring the reader to the brink of this precipice, and leave him there to continue the inquiry in ecumenical dialogues still to come.

MICHAEL POLANYI

The Scientific Revolution

ILLNESS has given me a chance to reconsider once more the theme which I have been asked to write about. During my stay in hospital there fell into my hands—by the kindness of its author—a book which has revealed to me a new, and I think much better, understanding of the situation we are facing today in consequence of the modern scientific revolution. The author is Josef Pieper, Professor of Philosophical Anthropology at the University of Münster, and his book which so impressed me is entitled *Scholastik*.[1] Owing to this book, I can see now that the conflict between faith and reason evoked by natural science today is but a modern variant of a problem which has filled the thoughts of men in other forms ever since the dawn of philosophic speculation 2,500 years ago.

You will notice that by dating the beginning of philosophy in the sixth century B.C., I am localizing this event in Greece and more particularly in Ionia and the Greek isles. I know this may be challenged and shall not argue it. Suffice it to say that, in my view, our anxiety about the relation between faith and reason here in Europe today is the legacy of a particular intellectual family. Modern science has recently been spreading this disturbance all over the planet, but it has formed no part of the heritage of Chinese or Hindu thought. It has originated with, and has

[1] Published in English by Pantheon Books, Inc., New York.

remained for two and a half millennia the preoccupation of, that part of humanity that has culturally centered mainly on Europe.

GREEK, MEDIEVAL, AND MODERN RATIONALISM

But even accepting these limits, the simplification I now see appearing before me may seem excessively sweeping. I see extending behind us three consecutive periods of rationalism, the Greek, the medieval, and the modern. Greek rationalism rose from a bed of mythopoeic thought. We may define this for brevity as a predominantly personal interpretation of all things. Myths and ritual couch most thoughts of men in terms of I-Thou and leave nothing of importance to be spoken of in terms of I-It. Greek speculative thought tended to liberate the mind from this personal network, by establishing a broad area of objective thought. It extended I-It relations into a new philosophic interpretation of things. In this Greek rationalism, reason was used for eroding and replacing traditional beliefs, unquestioningly held or tacitly taken for granted.

The Christian message exploded into this scene as an outrage to rationalism. It restored the relation of I to Thou to the center of everything. It proclaimed that a man put to death a few years before in a remote provincial capital was the Son of the Almighty God ruling the universe, and had atoned by his death for the sins of mankind. The Christian's duty was to believe in this event and be totally absorbed by its implications. Faith, faith that mocks reason, faith that scornfully declares itself to be mere foolishness in the face of Greek rationalism, is what St. Paul enjoins on his audiences.

The picture is familiar. But you may ask me where I see

any trace here of a new Christian, medieval rationalism, striving to reconcile faith with reason. It emerged later as this message spread among an intelligentsia steeped in Greek philosophy. It was to be formulated by St. Augustine in terms that became statutory for a thousand years after. Reason was declared ancillary to faith, supporting it up to the point where revelation took over, after which in its turn faith opened up new paths to reason. What Professor Pieper has shown to me for the first time is that the entire movement of scholastic philosophy from Boethius to William of Ockham was but a variation on this theme.

Ockham brought scholasticism to a close by declaring that faith and reason were incompatible and should be kept strictly separate. Thus he ushered in the period of modern rationalism, established on this division, with the proviso that reason alone can establish true knowledge. Henceforth, as John Locke was soon to put it, faith was no longer accepted as a higher power that reveals knowledge lying beyond the range of observation and reason, but as a mere personal acceptance which falls short of rational demonstrability. The mutual position of the two Augustinian levels was inverted.

In a way this step would have brought us back to Greek rationalism, and many of its authors did so regard it. They hoped that the new secular world view would appease religious strife and bring back the blessings of an antique dispassionate religious indifference. However, post-Christian rationalism soon entered on paths never trodden before by man, and we stand here today at the dismal end of this journey.

TOWARD A RESTORATION OF THE LOST HARMONY BETWEEN FAITH AND SCIENCE

But my purpose is not to denounce modern rationalism. The arts, the intellectual splendors, and moral attainments of the past three hundred years stand unrivaled in the history of mankind. The very failures and disasters that surround us may themselves bear testimony to this greatness. Only gigantic endeavor could precipitate us into such absurdities as the modern scientific outlook has made current today, and could set millions ablaze with a new bitterly skeptical fanaticism.

I shall take today these manifold and profoundly serious shortcomings of our present situation for granted, and shall bend all my effort to tracing a new line of thought along which, I believe, we may recover some of the ground rashly abandoned by the march of the modern scientific outlook. I believe indeed that this line of thought, if pursued systematically, may eventually restore the balance between belief and reason on lines essentially similar to those marked out by St. Augustine at the dawn of Christian rationalism.

I shall try to show you what I have in mind by speaking of the human person, and then expanding this into an analysis of discovery. Modern science and scientific philosophy cannot analyze the human person without reducing it to a machine. This flows from assuming that all mental processes are to be explained in terms of neurology, which in their turn must be represented as a chart of physical and chemical processes. The damage wrought by the modern scientific outlook is actually even more extensive: it tends towards replacing everywhere the personal I-Thou by an impersonal I-It.

Any attempt to restore a more sane and truthful view of the human person must go to the very roots of the conception of knowledge, and I shall start off in this direction by giving you an example to illustrate some of the essential features of knowledge which are disregarded by the modern conception of positive scientific knowledge.

THE TWO FORMS OF KNOWLEDGE

A few years ago a distinguished psychiatrist demonstrated to his students a patient who was having a mild fit of some kind. Later the class discussed the question whether this had been an epileptic or an hystero-epileptic seizure. The matter was finally decided by the psychiatrist: "Gentlemen," he said, "you have seen true epileptic seizure. I cannot tell you how to recognize it; you will learn this by more extensive experience."

This psychiatrist knew how to recognize this disease, but he was not at all certain how he did this. In other words, he recognized the disease by attending to its comprehensive appearance, and did so by relying on a multitude of clues which he could not clearly specify. Thus his knowledge of the disease differed altogether from his knowledge of these clues or symptoms. He recognized the disease by attending to it, while he was not attending to the symptoms in themselves, but only as clues. We may say that he was knowing the clues only by relying on them for attending to the pathological physiognomy to which they contributed. So if he could not tell what these clues were, while he could tell what the disease was, this was due to the fact that while we can always identify a thing we are attending to, and indeed our very attending identifies it, we cannot always identify the particulars on which we rely in our attending on the thing.

This fact can be generalized widely. There are vast domains of knowledge—of which I shall speak in a moment —that exemplify in various manners that we are in general unable to tell what particulars we are aware of when attending to a whole which they constitute. So we can declare that there are two kinds of knowing which invariably enter jointly into any act of knowing a comprehensive entity. There is (1) a knowing by attending to something, as we attend to the entity in question, and (2) a knowing by relying on our awareness of certain things in the way we rely on our awareness of the many particulars of the entity in the act of attending to it.

We can go further. Evidently, any attempt to identify the particulars of an entity would involve a shift of attention from the entity to the particulars. We would have to relax the attention given to the whole for the sake of discovering its particulars, which we had noticed until now only by being aware of them as parts of the whole. So that once we have succeeded in fully identifying these particulars, and are in fact attending to them now directly in themselves, we clearly shall not be relying any more on our awareness of them as particulars of a whole, and therefore will inevitably have lost sight of the whole altogether.

This fact is abundantly borne out by half a century of Gestalt psychology. We may put it as follows. It is not possible to be aware of a particular in terms of its contribution to a whole and at the same time to focus our attention on it in itself. Or again, since it is not possible to be aware of anything at the same time subsidiarily and focally, we necessarily tend to lose sight of an entity by attending focally to its particulars.

But we may add that this loss need not be definitive. We may successfully analyze the symptoms of a disease and concentrate our attention on its several particulars, and then return to our conception of its general appearance, by becoming once more subsidiarily aware of these particulars as constituent parts of the comprehensive picture of the disease. Indeed, such an oscillation of detailing and integrating is the royal road for deepening our understanding of any comprehensive entity.

KNOWING AND COMPREHENDING

In saying this, I have pronounced a key word. I have spoken of understanding. Understanding–comprehension: this is the cognitive faculty cast aside by a positivistic theory of knowledge, which refuses to acknowledge the existence of comprehensive entities as distinct from their particulars, and this is the faculty which I recognize as the central act of knowing. For comprehension can never be absent from any process of knowing, as it is indeed the ultimate sanction of any such act. What is not understood cannot be said to be known.

Lest this analysis appear too abstract, let me rapidly run through various forms of knowing to which it strikingly applies. I have so far used as my leading example the process of medical diagnostics. We have a closely similar process in the identification of the species to which an animal or a plant belongs. An expert who can identify 800,000 species of insects must rely on a vast number of clues which he cannot identify in themselves. This is why zoology and botany cannot be learned from printed pages, any more than medicine can. This is why so many hours of practical teaching in the laboratory has to be given also in many other branches of the natural sciences. Wherever this happens, there some knowledge of the comprehensive aspect of things is being transmitted, a knowledge of those things which we must acquire by becoming aware of a multitude of clues that cannot be exhaustively identified.

We must learn to identify the physiognomy of such things by relying on clues which cannot be clearly identified in themselves. But we hardly ever do such diagnosing without examining the object in question, and this testing itself has to be learned together with the physiognomies of the tested objects. We must jointly learn to be skillful testers as well as expert knowers. Actually, these are only two different and inseparable processes of comprehension. Expert knowing relies on a comprehension of clues, as skillful examination relies on a combination of tricks for tracing these clues.

SKILLS AND TOOLS

This reveals the structure of skills quite generally. A performance is called skillful precisely because we cannot clearly identify its component muscular acts. The craftsman's cunning consists in controlling these component acts jointly with a view to a comprehensive achievement. Such also is the sportsman's and musical performer's mastery. Neither can tell much, and mostly can tell very little, about the several muscular tricks he combines in accomplishing his art.

Skills usually require tools—instruments of some kind, and these are things patently akin to the particulars of a comprehensive entity. For they are tools or instruments by virtue of the very fact that we rely on them for accomplishing something to which we are attending by using the tool or instrument. In this case we can admittedly identify that on which we rely, though mostly we do not quite know how we actually use it. In any case, it still remains strikingly true that we cannot direct our attention to the thing on which we rely as our tool while relying on it for a skillful performance. You must keep your eye on the ball, and if you look at your racket instead, you inevitably lose the stroke. Any skillful performance is paralyzed by attending focally to its tools.

The same is true of speech. Listen to the sound of your words, while forgetting their context and meaning, which is the comprehensive entity which it is their function to subserve, and you will be instantly struck dumb. This brings in the whole multitude of signs, symbols, and gestures by which human communications are achieved and by the practical use of which the intelligence of man is developed far beyond that of the animals. Here is another vital area of skillful doing and knowing, all over which we are met with comprehensive entities to which we attend, and can attend only, by relying subsidiarily on things and acts of our own, to which we do not attend, and must not attend in themselves, for the time being.

PERCEPTION

We may add lastly that, deep down, in the most primitive forms of knowing, in the act of sensory perception, we meet with the very paradigm of the structure which I have postulated for all kinds of knowledge at all levels. It was indeed sensory perception, and particularly the way we see things, that has supplied Gestalt psychologists with material for their fundamental discoveries which I am expanding here into a new theory of knowledge. They have shown that our seeing is an act of comprehension for which we rely in a most subtle manner on clues from all over the field of vision, as well as on clues inside our body, supplied by the muscles controlling the motion of the eyes and the posture of the body. All these clues become effective only if we keep concentrating our attention on the objects we are perceiving. Many of the clues cannot be known in themselves at all, others can be traced only by acute scientific analysis, but all of them can serve the purpose of seeing what is in front of us only if we make no attempt to look at them or to attend to them in any way in themselves. They must be left to abide in the role of unspecifiable particulars of the spectacle perceived by our eyes, if we are to see anything at all.

This concludes my list. We have now before us the art of diagnostics and of the testing of objects to be diagnosed, as taught in universities; we have the practice of skills in general and the skillful use of tools in particular, which leads on to the use of words and other signs by which human intelligence is developed; and finally we have the act of perception, the most fundamental manifestation of intelligence, both in animals and men. In each of these cases we have recognized the typical elements of comprehension. I now want to show how this panorama of knowing suggests a new conception of knowledge, equally comprising both the I-It and the I-Thou, and establishing at the same time a new harmony between belief and reason.

KNOWLEDGE AND LEARNING

Clearly, the new element I have introduced here into the conception of knowing is the knowing of things by relying on our awareness of them for attending to something else that comprehends them. Now, we have an obvious experience of certain things which we know almost exclusively by relying on them. Our body is a collection of such things; we hardly ever observe our own body as we observe an external object, but continuously rely on it as a tool for observing objects outside and for manipulating these for our own purposes. Hence we may identify the knowing of something by attending to something else, as the kind of knowledge we have of our own body by living in it. This kind of knowing is not an I-It relation, but rather a way of existing, a manner of being. We might call it an I-Myself or I-Me relation.

We are, of course, born to live in our body and to feel that we are relying on it for our existence, but the more skillful uses of our body have to be acquired by a process of learning. For example, the faculty of seeing things by using our eyes is not inborn; it has to be acquired by a process of learning.

We may say then that when we get to know something as a clue, as a particular of a whole, as a tool, as a word, or as an element contributing to perception, by learning to rely on it, we do so in the same way as we learn to rely on our body for exercising intellectual and practical control over objects of our surroundings. So any extension of the area of reliance by which we enrich our subsidiary knowledge of things is an extension of the kind of knowledge we usually have of our body; it is indeed an extension of our bodily existence to include things outside it. To acquire new subsidiary knowledge is to enlarge and modify our intellectual being by assimilating the things we learn to rely on. Alternatively, we may describe the process as an act of pouring ourselves into these things.

These ways of acquiring knowledge may sound strange,

but then we are dealing with a kind of knowledge which, though familiar enough to us all, seems never to have been identified by students of the theory of knowledge. Evidently, all hitherto recognized processes for acquiring knowledge, whether based on experience or deduction, only apply to knowledge of things we are attending to, and not at all to what we know of things by relying on our awareness of them in the process of attending to something else. I shall continue, therefore, undeterred, my account of the way such knowledge is acquired and held, however curious this account may sound at first hearing.

KNOWLEDGE BY INDWELLING

When we rely on our awareness of some things for attending to something else, we may be said to have assimilated these things to our body. In other words, subsidiary knowledge is held by indwelling. Thus we comprehend the particulars of a whole in terms of the whole by dwelling in the particulars. We grasp the joint meaning of the particulars by dwelling in them.

My examples of comprehension will illustrate these conclusions. To diagnose a disease is to grasp the joint meaning of its symptoms, many of which we could not specify. These particulars we know subsidiarily by dwelling in them. Indwelling has a more obvious meaning when applied to a skillful testing of an object or any other feat of expert handling. Here we literally dwell in the innumerable muscular acts which contribute to our purpose, and this purpose is their joint meaning. Indwelling is most vivid in man's use of language. Human intelligence lives only by grasping the meaning and mastering the use of language. Little indeed of our mind lives in our natural body; our person comes into existence when our lips shape words and our eyes read print. The intellectual difference between a naked pigmy of Central Africa and a member of the French Academy is grounded in the cultural equipment by which Paris surpasses the African jungle. The French academician's superior personality is formed and manifested by his intelligent use of this superior equipment.

FOREKNOWING THE UNKNOWN

This brings us to the very threshold of our understanding of the way we know a human person. But let us consider first for a moment the way comprehension is achieved, as envisaged in the extended sense given to it by my examples. More often than not we comprehend things in a flash. But it is more instructive to think of the way we struggle from a puzzled incomprehension of a state of affairs toward its real meaning. The success of such efforts demonstrates man's capacity for knowing the presence of a hidden reality accessible to his understanding. The active foreknowledge of an unknown reality is the true motive and guide of discovery in every field of mental endeavor. The explicit forms of reasoning, whether deductive or inductive, are impotent in themselves; they can operate only as intellectual tools of the creative power residing in man's capacity to anticipate a hidden meaning of things.

This confidence in the hidden coherence of a puzzling state of affairs is guided by an external aid when a student is taught how to identify a disease or a specific biological specimen. When the psychiatrist in the example I mentioned said to his students that they will learn to recognize in practice the characteristic appearance of an epileptic seizure, he meant that they would learn to do so by accepting his own diagnosis of such cases and trying to understand what he based it on. All practical teaching, teaching of comprehension in all the senses of the term, is based on authority. The student must be confident that his master understands what he is trying to teach him and that he, the student, will eventually succeed in his turn in understanding the meaning of the things which are being explained to him.

Plato has argued that the task of solving a problem is logically absurd and therefore impossible. For if we already know the solution, there is no occasion to search for it, while if we don't know it, we can do nothing to find it, for we don't know then what we are looking for. The task of solving a problem is indeed self-contradictory, unless we admit that we can possess true intimations of the unknown. This is what Plato's argument proves, namely, that every advance in understanding is moved and guided by our fundamental power of seeing the presence of some hidden comprehensive entity behind the as yet incomprehensible clues which we see pointing toward this yet unknown entity. Our confidence in these powers of our own may arise from the depth of our own inquiring mind, or it may be guided by our confidence in the judgment of our masters. Yet it is always the same dynamic power, and its dynamics are akin to the dynamics of faith. Tillich says that "that which is meant by an act of faith cannot be approached in any other way than through an act of faith." And the same holds here. There is no other way of approaching a hidden meaning than by entrusting ourselves to our intimations of its yet unseen presence. These intimations are the only path toward enlarging our intellectual mastery over our surroundings.

A DYNAMIC CONCEPTION OF KNOWLEDGE

Tillich says that his dynamic conception of faith "is the result of conceptual analysis, both of the objective and subjective side of faith." This is precisely what I claim for my derivation of the dynamic conception of knowing. It is derived in the last resort from our realization of the two kinds of knowledge which combine to the understanding of a comprehensive entity when we rely on our awareness of particulars for our knowledge of the entity to which we are attending. Our awareness of the particulars is the personal, our knowledge of the entity the objective, element of knowing.

The dynamic force by which we acquire understanding is only reduced and never lost when we hold knowledge acquired by its impulse. It sustains the conviction for dwelling in this knowledge and for developing our thoughts within its framework. Live knowledge is a perpetual source of new surmises, an inexhaustible mine of still hidden implications. The death of Max von Laue a short while ago should remind us that his discovery of the diffraction of X-rays by crystals was universally acclaimed as an amazing confirmation of Boyle's speculation on the structure of crystals, which itself was a development of ideas originating with Lucretius and Epicurus. And Dalton's theory was amazingly confirmed in its turn by the experiments of J. J. Thompson eighty years later. To hold knowledge is indeed always a commitment to indeterminate implications, for human knowledge is but an intimation of reality, and we can never quite tell what reality will do next. It is external to us, it is objective, and, by the same token, its future manifestations can never be completely under our intellectual control.

So all true knowledge is inherently hazardous, just as all

true faith is a leap into the unknown. Knowing includes its own uncertainty as an integral part of it, just as, according to Tillich, all faith necessarily includes its own dubiety.

The traditional division between faith and reason, or faith and science (which Tillich reaffirms), reflects the assumption that reason and science proceed by explicit rules of logical deduction or inductive generalization. But I have said that these operations are impotent by themselves, and I could add that they cannot even be strictly defined by themselves. To know is to understand, and explicit logical processes are effective only as tools of a dynamic commitment by which we expand our understanding and then hold on to it. Once this is recognized, the contrast between faith and reason dissolves, and a close similarity of structure emerges in its place.

Admittedly, religious conversion commits our whole person and changes our whole being in a way that an expansion of natural knowledge does not do. But once the dynamics of knowing are recognized as the dominant principle of knowledge, the difference appears only as one of degree. For—as we have seen—all extension of comprehension involves an expansion of ourselves into a new dwelling place, of which we assimilate the framework by relying on it as we do on our own body. Indeed, the whole intellectual being of man comes into existence in this very manner, by absorbing the language and the cultural heritage in which he is brought up. The amazing deployment of the infant mind is stirred on by a veritable blaze of confidence sensing the hidden meanings of speech and other adult behavior and grasping these meanings. Moreover, the structure of the child's dynamic intellectual progress has its counterpart on the highest levels of creative achievement, and both these structures resemble closely that of the self-transformation entailed in a religious conversion.

FROM OBJECTIVE OBSERVATION
TO PERSONAL KNOWLEDGE

But a deeper division between reason and faith may be found in the urge toward objectivity which tends to break up the I-Thou axis of the religious world-view and establish everywhere I-It relations in its place. Has not the modern positivist outlook exercised its pressure even on the purely secular studies of the human mind, as well as of human affairs whether past or present, in favor of a mechanical conception of man which represents him as a bundle of appetites, or as a mechanical toy, or as a passive product of social circumstances?

It has, but this is due in my opinion to the obsessive limitation of knowledge to the outcome of explicit inferences. Persons can be identified only as comprehensive entities by relying on our awareness of numberless particulars, most of which we could never specify in themselves. This is the same process by which we diagnose an elusive illness or read a printed page. Just as we assimilate the symptoms of a disease by attending focally to the disease itself, and as we assimilate the printed text by attending to its meaning, so we assimilate the workings of another man's mind by attending to his mind. In this sense we may be said to know his mind by dwelling in its manifestations. Such is the structure of empathy (that I would prefer to call conviviality) which alone can establish a knowledge of other minds and indeed of any living being whatever.

Behaviorism tries to replace convivial knowledge by I-It observations of the particulars by which the mind of an individual manifests itself and tries to relate these particulars to each other by a process of explicit inference. But since most of the particulars in question cannot be observed in themselves at all and, in any case, their relation cannot be explicitly stated, the enterprise ends up by replacing its original subject by a grotesque simulacrum of it in which the mind itself is missing. The kind of knowledge which I am vindicating here, and which I call personal knowledge, casts aside these absurdities of the current scientific approach and reconciles the process of knowing with the act of addressing another person. In doing so it establishes a continuous ascent from our less personal knowing of inanimate matter to our convivial knowing of living beings, and beyond this to the knowing of our responsible fellow men. Such, I believe, is the true transition from the sciences to the humanities and also from our knowing the laws of nature to our knowing the person of God.

SCIENTIFIC AND CHRISTIAN
CONCEPTIONS OF MAN

But is the kind of person we may know in this manner not floating vaguely above its own bodily substance, outside of which it actually cannot exist at all? The answer to this question will reveal a surprising affinity between my conception of personhood and a central doctrine of Christianity.

I have said that the mind of a person is a comprehensive entity which is not specifiable in terms of its constituent particulars; but this is not to say that it can exist apart or outside of these particulars. The meaning of a printed page cannot be specified in terms of a chemical analysis of its ink and paper, but neither can this meaning be conveyed without the use of ink and paper. Though the laws of physics and chemistry apply to the particles of the body, they do not determine the manifestations of the mind; their function is to offer an opportunity for the mind to live and manifest itself. Our sense organs, our brain, the whole infinitely complex interplay of our organism offer to the mind the instruments for exercising its intelligence and judgment, and, at the same time, they restrict the scope of this enterprise, deflecting it by delusions, obstructing it by sickness, and terminating it by death.

The knowing of comprehensive entities establishes a series of ascending levels of existence, and the relationship I have just outlined obtains throughout between succeeding levels of this hierarchy. The existence of a higher principle is always rooted in the inferior levels governed by less comprehensive principles. Within this lower medium and by virtue of it, the higher principle operates freely, but not unconditionally, its range being restricted and its every action tainted by the lower principles on which it has to rely for exercising its own powers.

As the rising levels of existence were created by successive stages of evolution, each new level achieved higher powers entrameled by new possibilities of corruption. Our inanimate beginning was deathless, subject neither to failure nor suffering. From this have emerged levels of biotic existence subject to malformation and disease, and then, at higher stages, to illusion, to error, to neurotic affliction—finally to produce in man, in addition to all these liabilities, an ingrained propensity to do evil. Such is the necessary condition of a morally responsible being, grafted on a bestiality through which alone it can exercise its own powers.

Such is the inescapable predicament of man which theology has called his fallen nature. Our vision of redemption is the converse of this predicament. It is the vision of a man set free from this bondage. Such a man would be God incarnate; he would suffer and die as a man and by this very act prove himself divinely free from evil. This is the event, whether historic or mythical, which shattered the framework of Greek rationalism and has set for all times the hopes and obligations of man far beyond the horizon of here and now.

NATURAL AND SUPERNATURAL KNOWLEDGE

I have mentioned divinity and the possibility of knowing God. These subjects lie outside my argument. But my conception of knowing opens the way to them. Knowing, as a dynamic force of comprehension, uncovers at each step a new hidden meaning. It reveals a universe of comprehensive entities which represent the meaning of their largely unspecifiable particulars. A universe constructed as an ascending hierarchy of meaning and excellence is very different from the picture of a chance collocation of atoms to which the examination of the universe by explicit modes of inference leads us. The vision of such a hierarchy inevitably sweeps on to envisage the meaning of the universe as a whole. Natural knowing expands continuously into supernatural knowing.

The very act of scientific discovery offers a paradigm of this transition. It is a passionate pursuit of a hidden meaning, guided by an intensely personal foreknowledge of this hidden reality. The intrinsic hazards of such efforts are of its essence; discovery is defined as an advancement of knowledge that cannot be achieved by any application of explicit modes of inference, however diligent. Yet the discoverer must labor night and day. For though no labor can make a discovery, no discovery can be made without intense, absorbing, devoted labor. Here we have, in paradigm, the Pauline scheme of faith, works, and grace. The discoverer works in the belief that his labors will prepare his mind for receiving a truth from sources over which he has no control. I regard the Pauline scheme, therefore, as the only adequate conception of scientific discovery.

Such is, in bold outline, my program for reconsidering the conception of knowledge and restoring thereby the harmony between faith and reason. Few of the clues which are guiding me today were available to the scholastics. The modes of reasoning which they relied on were inadequate; their knowledge of nature was poor and often spurious. Moreover, the faith they wanted to prove to be rational was cast into excessively rigid and detailed formulas, presenting intractable and sometimes even absurd problems to the reasoning mind.

Even so, though their enterprise collapsed, it left great monuments behind it. I believe that we are today in an infinitely better position to renew their basic endeavor. The present need for it could not be more pressing. We should therefore spare no effort for advancing this enterprise.

JEAN LADRIÈRE

Faith and the
Technician Mentality

THE PROGRESSIONIST SPIRIT

The technician mentality and the atheistic spirit. As
there are many things to say about the relationship between
the life of faith and the technician mentality, I shall have
to select, and I propose to speak about what seems to me to
be a particularly important aspect of the content of the
technician mentality—and I will explain what I mean by
this—"the progressionist spirit." As I understand it, the
purpose of this lecture is not so much to talk about what
technological life can mean for the believer, the Christian,
but rather to analyze the content of the technician mentality so as to state the problem that we must then discuss
together, the problem of what technology means for the
Christian. Since this is the point which we must reach in
the end, I shall begin by stating a fact, which seems to me
extremely important, about technology, or rather about the
technician mentality, and that is the connection which is
becoming evident today between the technician mentality
and the atheistic spirit. So, I make it clear from the start
what is the most radical and difficult aspect of the problem:
I state it in its most extreme form. That seems to me the
way to shed light on the matter. There is a connection,
then, between the technician mentality and the atheistic
spirit, the atheistic mentality, a connection which is some-

times veiled, implicit, and in some cases perfectly explicit, positive, claimed. In the communist world, atheism is certainly related explicitly, and in the most avowed manner, to science and technology; in any case it is related to the interpretation of science and technology.

In the earlier Marxism, in what I feel tempted to call paleo-Marxism, there were certain thoughts about atheism, but what to me seems very striking is that the atheism of today has little to do with this paleo-Marxist atheism. The atheism of today seems to represent itself as a scientific position, a sort of victory of the scientific spirit. And atheist propaganda seems to make use—if not exclusively at least by preference—of arguments drawn from science, and from the results of technology and its applications. These arguments, moreover, are extremely simplistic, and they may make you smile, but what is important is the mentality which they reveal. I think at this point, for instance, of an argument used in Soviet literature, which explains that it is quite certain that heaven cannot be inhabited by God, as has always been said, because now we launch sputniks into it, and it is obvious that "heaven" is a space in which man can move; in fact it is space which belongs to man— and if it belongs to man it does not belong to God; it is a legend, a mythical picture. Of course, this is a ridiculous argument! But if it is used, we must suppose that it makes an impression on people who have neither theological nor scientific education, and are perhaps not aware that in the use of the word "heaven" there is a play upon words. However this may be, in spite of its somewhat ridiculous character, this argument, and other similar ones, reveals a state of mind, a mentality in which the atheistic attitude appears to be related to the technician's attitude. The same relation also exists outside the communist world. It is doubtless a relationship which remains in general implicit, which is not the subject of an affirmation, which is not the concern of propaganda, and of which those in whom it is to be found are perhaps not fully conscious; but it is no less a relation which we can easily observe around us. We all know some research workers for whom the practice of applied science, or of technics simply, seems to be all they need to live for, and which above all quite obscures for them the domain of the religious life. The religious problems of which they are aware because people in their circle discuss them, seem to them devoid of meaning, uninteresting; and, without being exactly hostile, they are quite indifferent to these questions, just as they are also, it must be said, to philosophical questions. Philosophy seems to them like empty chatter, and, a fortiori if I may say so, theology seems to them to be senseless.

Liberation and the revolutionary spirit. But, if we want to plumb the technician mentality, we must perhaps introduce a third term alongside technology and atheism, and this third term seems rather more related to the movement of modern societies. To describe it I would suggest the word "liberation" or "liberty." Men proclaim, in all parts of the world, that they want to liberate themselves. They want to liberate themselves from exploitation, from external or internal domination; they want to liberate themselves from poverty, from the weight of their natural necessities. It matters little here the concrete forms this demand takes; it is enough to recognize that there is certainly everywhere in the world today this demand for liberty. And the very term, the very word "liberty," is almost a magic word which acts powerfully upon hearts and minds. There is perhaps a myth after all, a myth of liberty and liberation; we cannot go into it now, but I am observing a fact: the power of this word and perhaps of this myth. Naturally, if we speak of liberty or of liberation, this in itself immediately evokes certain revolutionary movements, and so what we may call the "revolutionary spirit." There is on all sides in the world today a revolutionary spirit, which shows up now here now there, but which is certainly active everywhere. A revolutionary spirit, using the term in its most general sense, is a spirit which aims at rather fundamental changes in society. We see that there is a certain connection—I would not wish to say a complete connection—between these three terms: atheism, revolutionary spirit in the sense which I have explained, and technician mentality. I repeat that this connection is sometimes affirmed quite explicitly —and this is what happens in the case of communism—and sometimes it is just lived more or less silently.

From archaic to industrial societies. If this connection exists, we are perhaps called upon to ask which of these three terms is the most important, which supplies the motive force. Here I have the impression that the most important is technology, and that the two others are only a sort of mask. Obviously this is a debatable interpretation; I put it forward simply as a hypothesis. We may indeed ask whether the key to all these contemporary phenomena does not lie, quite simply, in the fact that we are in the presence of a vast transformation of human societies which, as Father Teilhard de Chardin said, must pass out of the neolithic stage (which was typified by the existence of preponderantly agricultural societies) into the industrial stage. What has been happening during the last century and a half is a switch of humanity towards a new type of society based essentially on industry. We could support this thesis by appealing to many facts in contemporary history. I will quote one of these which seems rather impressive to me: Marxism is a revolutionary theory, born in an industrial country, and appearing as an interpretation of the evolution of industrial societies. At the present time, a hundred years after the appearance of the Marxist theory, we observe that no industrial country has become communist, in any case not by its own efforts, but we observe also that the countries which have become communist are those which, at the moment when they did so, were not at all industrialized, or were only beginning to be so. We may therefore ask whether the profound forces, the hidden dynamisms, which used communism as a sort of mythical veneer, had not precisely this significance, that they led to the rise of industrial societies, to the transformation of archaic societies into industrial societies. And now, what we call the problem of the underdeveloped continents seems largely to be the problem of the transformation of backward societies into industrial societies by one means or another. Moreover, one has increasingly the impression that what interests man is the means rather than the doctrines. Communism, which was a sort of philosophical luxury for industrialized countries, a subject for philosophical or moral debate, today stands in these underdeveloped countries for a more or less efficacious technique: it is judged not on its philosophical or moral content, but, it seems to me, on the efficiency which it represents.

So, it seems more and more that the real criterion which men tend to apply is not so much (as it perhaps was during the last century and still perhaps is in advanced countries) a moral, theoretical, ideological criterion, but a criterion of efficiency. What they want, at all costs, is to catch up with the advanced countries by the most rapid means. Naturally, it is not only for pleasure that they want to catch up, nor simply to imitate the advanced countries, but because there seems to be today in the world a model for social organization which has become imperative, and that is the industrial model. What we call an "advanced society"—the expression itself is revealing—is simply a society which has already gone far along the road of industrialization. There is something curious in the conflicts which rage in the contemporary world: witness the cold war for example. Obviously the cold war has many aspects. There are of course the political and the ideological ones, but there are also the technological aspects. The cold war is in part a war of technicians: who will be the first to find a more powerful bomb, who will be the first to find a more effective rocket which cannot be intercepted, or at any rate intercepted in time? One has the impression, if one stands back a little from the struggle, that one effect among others of the cold war has been to encourage a considerable development of certain techniques such as atomic and rocket techniques. We may indeed ask whether anyone would have made so great an effort, for example in the rocket field, if there had been no cold war. So one may imagine a sort of evil genius pushing men into certain lines of research. As men's inertia is very great, what I may call "indirect motivations" must be brought into play. An appeal to the direct motivation would consist in saying, "Look how interesting it is to travel in inter-stellar space; don't you think it would be worth while to work for such a project?" Well, a speech like that would have had little success! The answer would have been, "Of course, it would be very interesting." But nothing more would have happened. To produce an effect, appeal had to be made to indirect and powerful motivations, to motivations which stir the emotions. And there is one emotion which is always effective, and that is fear. We see that the result has been excellent: the use of the emotion of fear has led certain societies to agree to considerable sacrifices of money, effort, and man-power to perfect exactly these techniques. Naturally, we do not know all that will come out of it. We all hope that it will be something other than war, something more than military weapons, but we may well ask whether this would have been accessible without the presence of threats and without the military objectives which are, after all, the principal objectives of this research.

I think we could find many examples of this kind. We could find many arguments converging in this direction and showing that the real concern is the transformation of human societies into industrial societies: the industrialization of the world, the constitution of a universal technological society, that is to say, a universal society for the domination of the earth. When I say "universal society," I do not necessarily mean "a society organized on a world basis," something like a world state. I simply mean a society where, in effect, all men, all human groups, are included in the mechanism of industrialization. There is in practice no place today for a group which wishes to stay behind, which would rather hold on to neolithic or archaic forms of existence. There have been, and still are, such groups, but we know that they amount only to a few individuals, and that they are doomed to disappear sooner or later. And this is what suggested to me the idea of an evil genius, who uses human emotions, conflicts, revolutions, ideologies, moral concepts, in order to reach finally an end which we are beginning to descry, and which is exactly this transformation, this sort of global mutation of humanity in its march towards a new kind of society, whose exact nature we do not yet see clearly.

The rational element in "progressivism." So if we want

to sum up all this, if we would try to discover what these three terms have in common—technician mentality, the demand for liberty, and the atheistic spirit—it seems to me that we might suggest the word "progressivism." There is a progressivist mentality in the world of today, and particularly in technology, if it is true that it is technology which in the final analysis constitutes the basic factor. What is this progressivist mentality? One can easily see what is meant, but it is not so easy to define. It seems to me that it is necessary to distinguish in it a rational element and an emotional element. There is in progressivism a rational element, and it is simply the setting to work of the possibilities of reason. It is the bias towards approaching every situation in which man finds himself with the instruments of a rational analysis, with the instruments of a reason which feels sufficiently sure of itself to think that it can solve all problems, that there always is a solution to problems; for which every problem that has a meaning has, because of that very fact, a solution. One will hear talk of this principle: that it is only the problems that can be solved that have any meaning. Behind this mentality, there is, of course, a certain new form of rationalism which is making its appearance: reason now appears to be related to the possibility of solving problems. So, reason is interpreted from the point of view of action and no longer, as in antiquity, from the point of view of *theoria,* a contemplation of the world. It is not so much, or not chiefly, a question of pulling out the intelligible tissue of the world, of describing the intelligibility of the world, but of actually *making* the intelligibility of the world, that is, of making apparent in an effective way this rational and intelligible fiber that is in things. Now, this mentality today is no longer the affair of a few specialists, but one could almost say that it is the mentality of the man in the street. I am always rather astonished to hear people who know nothing about science say, when one speaks to them about difficult questions which preoccupy us, "Oh, we shall find some way." They are sure that we shall find some answer, no matter what. We can speak to them about the most difficult problems, and they are still sure that we shall find some way out. Thus an extraordinary sense of security has taken possession of the modern man, because he is convinced that we shall always find a way, that there is no limit to the possibilities of finding solutions.

The emotional element in "progressivism." But naturally, in this progressivist spirit, there is also an emotional element; this is a sort of impatience, almost, I would say, an instability of the mind, the feeling that one must not become attached to an acquisition, that one cannot stand still, that it is almost an evil, a moral failing, to stand still, that there is an obligation to try something new, to plunge into new formulas, to change. The idea, for example, that there could be oilfields unexploited somewhere seems criminal, absurd, abominable. All available energy should be exploited; it is a sort of collective duty. The idea that there are human groups who would wish to oppose this also appears abominable; these groups should be converted or even eliminated; it is intolerable that there should be unexploited wealth anywhere in the world, or energies not yet harnessed. And here I think of a very fine comparison by Heidegger in a work on technology. He says, "For the poet Hoelderlin, the Rhine was not a river, but in a certain sense a god." This thought indeed is expressed in Hoelderlin's famous poem on Father Rhine. He saw it still from the point of view of a poetic cosmology, or shall we say a cosmic pantheism. For contemporary man, and for the engineer who is the paradigm of contemporary man, the Rhine is an object in which we can usefully sink turbines to provide electric current. And so on. The Rhine was a good example to characterize the mentality of modern man who is impatient to reduce everything to the state of a useful object. That it what I would call the emotional element in progressivism.

THE TECHNICIAN MENTALITY

Up until now, I have tried to paint a great backcloth, to attach the technician mentality to a sort of fundamental spirit which inhabits the world of today. Now I would like to consider more especially technology, the mentality of the technician, leaving aside for the time being the other factors of which I have spoken. I shall do it in three parts. I shall speak first of the nature of the technical project; then of the dangers inherent in it; finally to the values which it contains; and that will enable me in conclusion to link up again with our preoccupation, which is the significance of technology for the Christian.

THE NATURE OF THE TECHNICAL PROJECT

An enterprise on the march. Let us ask ourselves first, what is the nature of the technical project? Let us say, to begin with, that it is a project in the proper sense of the word, that is, an enterprise on the march, an enterprise which is going somewhere, which is orientated in a certain direction. In other terms, technology is not only a series of operations, or a complex of inventions, or a set of partial methods, but it is really a total collective enterprise, a system in movement, which has a meaning and consequently a unity. There is an immanent meaning which makes its unity. Only this project is a project which remains implicit; I mean that nobody would be capable now of saying exactly what he wants. And of course a fortiori, in the past, nobody would have been capable of saying exactly what he wanted. Doubtless they wanted certain things; in other terms, they had objectives, but these objectives were—and remain—always relatively limited. We have also a presentiment that behind these objectives we will find other objectives, but I do not think we can say that we have a view of the whole, nor that we have a clear view of the finality towards which we are moving. We are therefore somewhat in the position of a swimmer who has dived into a current: he knows very well that there is a current, he knows how he ought to swim in this current, but he does not know whether he will finally arrive at a waterfall where he will be broken to pieces, or whether he will come to a big lake where he will find a marvelous view. We do not know very well what awaits us. Yet we can nevertheless discern certain elements; we can see upon what this enterprise is based, and we can after all say something about the direction in which we are going, in so far as we discover it indicated in the movement itself.

The basis of the enterprise. And now, what is the basis of our enterprise? It is based on the discovery of the potential character of the world which is offered us. We have progressively discovered that the world which is given us, that is, nature, is not a pure datum, but is, in a sense, incomplete; that there are certain incoherent elements in it which are possibilities, potentialities, and open potentialities, and that our effort may take its bearings on these potentialities, and may actualize them. In other terms, we have discovered the possibility of an actualization of the potentialities of nature, and this discovery soon created the feeling of a duty: we end by having the feeling that, if this possibility exists, it is our duty to complete, so to speak, the movement of nature by directing our effort upon the natural potentialities, so as to draw out of them what, of herself and left to her own resources, nature could not have given. A very good image of this is electricity. An electric current does not exist as such in nature; but, on the other hand, nature has the where-withal for making electric current. Only for this purpose a certain mediation is required; certain conceptual and material apparatus must be constructed.

The direction of the enterprise. Now, if such is the basis of the enterprise, whither is it going, what is its direction? There is a very limited objective which is normally suggested—utility. Everyone says: all these inventions, all these new resources, are very useful to man because they improve his living conditions. For example, the internal combustion engine enables men to travel faster, further, in larger numbers, and of course that may be considered to be useful up to a certain point. Here, one may say that progress, or the progressivist demon of whom I spoke a little while ago, again makes use of an emotive element—laziness. If there are automobiles, one need not walk any more, so it is less tiring. But perhaps this is only an illusion. The sociologists say that we work today harder than ever, that in earlier times there was chronic under-employment, just because of a lack of resources, whereas now that there are resources, there is rather a tendency to over-work. So this element of laziness is very relative. Let us say that it only provides a sort of bait: the progressivist demon doubtless uses this utilitarian bait to send us further. In other terms, the satisfaction of certain needs does no more than create other needs, so that we are started on an endless spiral, and when we think we may be able to work less, in fact we shall perhaps work still harder. Besides, this idea of utility does not get us very far, and we begin to see this very well today, since contemporary technology is becoming less and less utilitarian. I would say that technology is becoming a speculative technology. In fact, it seems to me that in the most spectacular contemporary achievements the utilitarian aspect is after all rather negligible. People who insist on utility say, "Certainly, but it could all have a military use." But can we call this utility? It would be better to talk of experiment—of a rather monstrous experiment too, an experiment whose real nature we do not even know very accurately. In any case, it seems to me that we could more accurately speak of a speculative technology, of a technology which, in the sphere of action is becoming what science appeared to be yesterday in the sphere of pure thought. And this is perhaps most visible in the most developed of the sciences. Physics, for example, can no longer do without extremely powerful instruments, which, moreover, count among the finest contemporary technical achievements. Scientific research and technical research started off in harness together and have become inseparable, and what once appeared to be a utility has become in some sense a by-product, a side-effect. The important thing, the thing which in any case mobilizes the minds of the most alert technicians, the finest examples of the technician mentality, is precisely the speculative character of the enterprise.

In reality, we do not know very clearly where we are going, what all this is going to reveal in the end, what it will all finally make possible. Those who want to predict begin to talk about a civilization of leisure, and one has the impression that in so doing they are trying to find a justification. As in the past humanism and culture were highly esteemed—and by culture one meant belles-lettres —and as on the other hand technology has become essential, one tries to find a justification, saying, "Of course, we must now for the time being immerse ourselves in technology; we shall have no time for literature; but we shall come back to it with all the more enthusiasm later because we shall have more time, and then everybody will be able to read the classics!" But this seems to me a retrospective way of looking at the future; it is looking at the future with the eyes of the past, and it is also perhaps a way of giving oneself a sense of security, because obviously an indescribable future can only create a feeling of insecurity. So, one seeks to find calm by trying to picture the future, and of course one can only picture it to oneself with images of the past. In a sense, one imagines the future as a sort of generalization of what existed formerly in certain aristocratic groups. One imagines the future as being the democratization of Athenian thought!

But there are already very profound modifications which have affected human existence, and these are, in one sense, irreversible; in particular, technical developments have permitted an increase in the population, have permitted much denser concentrations of people to live in certain areas, and here is obviously an irreversible phenomenon. There is no question, for instance, of an industrial country returning to the neolithic stage. We can see, for instance, how senseless were certain American plans for turning the German people back into a pastoral community after the 1939-45 war. It is impossible to make an industrial people live as they did 500 years ago; that is quite clear.

The techniques of human relations. In any case, what has happened, and continues to happen, is a definitive break with nature. More and more, human effort is directed to man himself, or, more accurately, to society itself, and no longer to nature. At the beginning, naturally, it is essentially upon nature that human effort is concentrated, because man is still quite unequipped. But as soon as he has made himself an instrument, he applies his energies more and more to society itself, that is, to the organization of human relations, to the way men represent to themselves their life, their future, and the use they make of the objects which are at their disposal. This seems to be very clear in certain techniques of manipulation, for example, the techniques of propaganda, of publicity, of what we call "human relations." Increasingly we see that this is what is important. American sociologists insist upon this fact; they say that what characterizes contemporary American man is precisely that he is socialized man, and that the new techniques are applied much more to the manipulation of human relations than to nature. One could say that the problem of the domination of nature has already been resolved; now a new phase is appearing, the phase of the conditioning of social groups, the adjustment of groups to each other and of individuals to groups. This adjustment is no longer left to chance; we no longer leave it to automatic mechanisms, but resort to carefully thought out manipulation. Human relations are thus made the object of a technique in the proper sense of the word, and a technique based on a science. We must survey here the whole field of what we could call the human techniques—the psychological techniques, on the one hand, and the social techniques, on the other. It is certain that we are looking for procedures for the adjustment of individuals to groups, and of groups to each other. I think, for instance, of depth psychology. There is still, of course, a good deal of discussion about depth psychology, but there is certainly one interpretation of it which sees it as a means of adjusting the individual to the group. The individual who presents neurotic symptoms, who is no longer completely in control of his behavior, is interpreted as an individual who is not adjusted to the group. We do not say that he is not adjusted to nature, but that he is no longer adjusted to the group, to the culture, in which he lives. To cure him, we have recourse to a certain technique of human relations—a technique which is itself a human relation. No instruments are employed; it is a technique using speech only, one which brings a human relation to bear on the subject. It is thought that by such a technique it is possible to rediscover for a neurotic individual a suitable, balanced insertion in the group to which he belongs. Similarly, what we call the techniques of human relations are techniques which make it possible, or will make it possible, to regulate relations between groups.

THE DANGERS OF THE TECHNICIAN MENTALITY

The concentration of power and human decision. All this development contains a certain measure of danger. In the first place, the increase of the instruments of power in our hands to deal with external nature and social nature, evidently creates an increased responsibility. When we have no instruments, we are largely at the mercy of what we call fate—fatality—the play of laws which control the natural processes; for example, we are at the mercy of drought and famine. As soon as we have instruments at our disposal, human decisions must intervene. And the more powerful the instruments the more important the decisions are, because indetermination increases; it increases because the resources are numerous and some are not innocent.

We must establish a balance-sheet of possible gain and possible loss, calculating that if we adopt such and such a measure there will be such and such a result, but that at the same time it will destroy a certain equilibrium, and so on. We know what unconsidered application of certain methods of agriculture has cost: for example, a bad use of modern agricultural methods has caused soil erosion. Or again, the use of DDT has banished the insects which fertilize certain flowers, and thus caused the disappearance of certain plants. What is true for nature is also true for man. We do not exactly know what is the internal effect upon individuals of certain methods which we use. I shall cite here only one very massive illustration—the atom bomb. There was a day when men had to take a decision on this subject. It was known that the use of an atom bomb was possible. Were they going to use it? That depended entirely on a human decision. There was no natural law here; they did not have to abandon themselves to fate; they could say "yes," or they could say "no." There were moreover conflicting opinions; there was a discussion, and finally there was a decision. From that moment an important step was taken: we entered the atomic era. What must be noted is that this decision is at once collective and individual. It is collective because it clearly interests the whole world; it is individual in the sense that it rests usually on the shoulders of a few. In the case of the atom bomb, it was in the last resort one man, the President of the United States at that time, who had to take the ultimate decision. What is very striking in contemporary society is the extreme concentration of power in the hands of a very small number of men, and the considerable burden of responsibility which is attached to certain functions. Here lies the sociological aspect. But there is also the moral aspect: we may ask ourselves if men are effectively prepared to face increased responsibilities for themselves and their descendants (for very often these responsibilities concern men of the future as well as those now living). For we continually face problems of this kind. Here is another example: you all remember the controversy in Italy a few months ago because some research worker had tried to develop artificially a human embryo. Was this permissible? Clearly there is an ethical problem here. But obviously also the progressivist spirit to which I have referred before would come out unconditionally in favour of the experiment: not only could one make it, but one must.

The reduction of man to the status of object. The second danger is the tendency to reduce man to the status of object. Since techniques are not only instruments for the domination of nature, but also instruments for conditioning and manipulating man and human groups, one naturally comes to consider man as a fragment of nature, as an object. The experiment of which I just spoke is an illustration of this mentality, of this attitude. Man reduces himself to the status of subject of an experiment. He tends to empty out the spiritual and ethical content of the human being and to see in himself nothing more than an object for study. Of course, we justify it by saying that it is for his greater good, and for the greater good of future generations, as though the greater good of future generations should follow as a matter of course from an unconditioned development of technology.

The nihilism of the technician. A third danger seems to me deeper and more serious. The development of the technician mentality is related to the power mentality—to seek to control as completely as possible nature in and outside ourselves is obviously to seek an increase of power. But this power-centered mentality, this quest for power, depending on the resources of rational analysis, with all the patience and humility that it presupposes at the same time, leads pretty often to an obscuring of the question of significance. Norbert Wiener, the founder of cybernetics, has expressed this admirably in a work called *The Human Use of Human Beings:* "We have learned to answer the question *how,* but we are no longer capable of answering the question *why.*" We have accumulated a vast store of know-how, but we cannot even tell ourselves for what object we shall use it. It is an admirable way of saying that we are no longer capable of answering the question of meaning. But we have to go further: it must be said that we are no longer capable of seeing that there is a question of meaning. It must be said that we are tempted to consider that finalities can in a sense look after themselves; that finalities are taken for granted; that they are inherent in the very effort which we exhibit, in the enterprise itself in which we are engaged. And I think that this attitude finally leads to what we could call the nihilism of the technician, because there is such a nihilism. I would say that there is nihilism as soon as the finalities are slurred over, as soon as there are no longer any effective finalities. Obviously, human action necessarily entails finalities. If anyone makes an experiment, he is looking for something—therefore there is finality. If someone constructs a piece of apparatus, it is because he wants a result, to know whether his apparatus works. There is always finality in the action in the sense that the action has objectives. Only the objectives of technical action are objectives which must remain very limited, short-term objectives, giving the impression of "pseudo-finalities." In other terms, the effort of the technician becomes its own justification, its own finality. There is no occasion to ask why or wherefore; it is evident that one must do what existing techniques make possible. But it is in doing this that he finds his justification, that he justifies and authenticates himself. Naturally this nihilistic situation is generally masked. What characterizes this forgetfulness of meaning is that the forgetfulness is not conscious as such. As Heidegger said, in his study of the essence of technology, man has not only lost sight of the question of meaning, but he no longer knows even that he has lost it. Heidegger develops this idea in his commentary on a poem of Hoelderlin in which occurs this sentence: *Les dieux se sont enfuis.* Not only have they fled, says Heidegger, but we have lost all trace of them, we do not know whither they have fled. We do not even know that there have been gods. The world is totally desacralized, but it no longer knows that it is. Man is in distress—for at bottom nihilism is distress—but he no longer knows that he is; he is no longer capable of knowing. But there are after all some pointers, some symptoms, we might say, which are beginning to make their appearance in the world of today, and which seem indirectly to show just this situation of distress. For example, one such symptom is the apparently aberrant behavior seen especially among groups of young people in highly industrialized countries. We enquire into this, we talk about the *nouvelle vague,* the *blousons noirs,* the beatniks. Every country has its own expression for this phenomenon: in Poland and Russia they talk of "hooligans," in England of "teddy boys." But I wonder if we should not see in all these phenomena some symptoms (among others, because there are others, but these are particularly obvious ones) of an inner emptiness, which is precisely nihilism, the collapse of meaning. There are also other symptoms, which are perhaps less apparent, or less obviously pathological in character, but which are no less symptoms of a pathological existential situation. Much of the behavior of contemporary man is insensate behavior, which manifests the absence of meaning. And moreover much of this behavior involves the insensate use of technical instruments, for example, the radio, television, means of transport. It seems to me that certain ways of using these instruments manifest the character *in-sensé* of contemporary existence.

The disappearance of the sacred and the devaluation of the symbol. Now, another phenomenon related to all this is the disappearance of the "sacred." If we can solve all these problems, if it is only the problems which can be solved that have meaning, that means in the last resort that what remains of meaning is the same as a realizable operation, an operation, therefore, of a technical nature. It is the new interpretation of reason to which I have already alluded. That necessarily brings with it a desacralization of the world; there is no longer any mystery; there is no longer any reference to any transcendence whatever; the world is spread out before us like some kind of transparent material, and if it is not quite transparent yet, then it certainly will soon be so. In principle, everything is already transparent: there is nothing that we cannot do or that is not offered to our consciousness. At the same time as this disappearance of the sacred, there is also a sort of devaluation of certain types of language, which are not those of technology: symbolic language for example. The devaluation of the symbol, of the sign: the sign is a tangible reality, but the meaning refers to something else, the non-visible which is not, however, the unsayable. Now the technological mentality does not use the symbol, or if it speaks of a symbol it is in quite a different sense, in the mathematical sense, which is then quite another thing. But the comprehension of a sign as a sign thus becomes difficult, if not impossible, for one who is used to deciphering nature directly, according to a method which gives a certain answer after a certain number of manipulations. But then this has extremely serious consequences from the point of view of the religious mentality, precisely because religious realities are only accessible through a language which uses signs and symbols. There is no way of transmitting religious reality through the language of technology. In proportion as we make ourselves impermeable to religious language, we naturally make ourselves impermeable to the realities which it seeks to reveal through this language.

THE VALUES OF THE TECHNICIAN MENTALITY

The greater possibility of justice. However, if technology involves these dangers, it also conceals certain values. It carries with it a value, first of all, from the point of view of the evolution of society, for after all it is very possible that technology will help us to solve what we may call the "social problem" and the problem of justice—will help us to give everybody an equal measure of these resources, whether in relation to the domination of nature and the satisfaction of their primary needs or to the possibilities of culture. In a situation of scarcity, there is every chance of inequality, but in a situation of plenty, there is more chance of true equality. I say "there is more chance" because after all it is not absolutely inevitable; in other words, there are moral conditions which remain indispensable. But the resources now exist to give to all equivalent possibilities. And for this very reason, the utilization of technology on the plane of social organization certainly carries with it a great ethical potential.

The development of personality. Technology has also a

value on the level of the development of the personality, for if it is true that the development of our power over the external world may lead to the abolition of the question of meaning, at the same time it must be said that the development of this power over the external world may also lead to a sharper development of self-consciousness and all that it involves. There is a solidarity here between two movements: the movement of technology which takes us outwards, but in such a way as to affirm our power, and another movement which brings us back upon ourselves so as to discern ourselves as the source of this power. This double movement has been particularly easy to see, it seems to me, in European thought since the seventeenth century. In a very curious way, it has often been those who were at the origin of modern science and technology who have also been the philosophers of conscience. At the same time as they contributed to the affirmation of man's power over the external world, man's control over his environment, they became sensitive to the inner force which is within man, the power of conscience as both thought and liberty. So, we see very well what technology can contribute on the side of culture, on condition that this solidarity is recognized; the conquest of an increased power over the environment may well go together with a sort of inner conquest of thought and of liberty.

The roots of a new humanism. Thirdly, from the point of view of humanism, the development of this power evidently changes the significance of man's situation in relation to the cosmos. Instead of feeling himself powerless in face of a more or less hostile nature—not wholly hostile, say partially hostile—man now changes his relation to nature and feels himself to be a sort of demiurge, a being called to modify the face of nature, and to modify it in a coherent manner according to the laws which he discovers. He does not, of course, modify it in a capricious or arbitrary manner, but in a rational manner, following, so to speak, the dotted lines written in nature herself. He draws a continuous line between the dots. Nature is not offered as a complete, penetrable whole, but as an invitation. Nature invites us to undertake an operation whose character we can at first distinguish only dimly, but as we follow the line we gradually find a design emerging. Naturally this is probably leading us to a new way of envisaging our relations with the cosmos, to a new vision of the cosmos itself, and, as a result, also to a new vision of man inside the cosmos. One might therefore say that here are the roots of a new humanism.

The spiritual value of technology. Finally, the fourth positive aspect of technology: from the religious point of view we may say that the technician mentality contains a dynamic aspect which seems to be closely related to the profound dynamism which is inherent in Christianity, which *is* Christianity itself. So much so that we may ask ourselves whether technology, even where it appears to be linked up with atheism, is not a deeply Christian phenomenon. But I do not mean by that, naturally, that technology is the direct consequence of the development of Christianity. It is understood that there are in man natural powers and that the development of technology is precisely the development of certain of these natural powers. Technological man only unfolds all these natural potentialities; in other terms, the enterprise of technology is certainly a work of reason. But we may still ask whether, taking a longer view, looking deeper, this sort of dynamism, this sense of movement, this "progressivist" spirit which dwells in us— especially this sense of duty of which we spoke earlier—

are not all profoundly and secretly bound up with the presence in humanity, through the fact of the Redemption, of a mysterious dynamism which, in the last resort, is not that of reason but of grace. What could perhaps bring us to think this is the comparison between, on the one hand, the attitude towards technology which Christianity makes possible, and, on the other, that which could be taken by a Buddhist, for example. I said "could," and I use the conditional because I think it would be an exaggeration to interpret too precisely the Buddhist position, for it would not, as I understand, be impossible for a Buddhist to welcome technology. So I speak in the conditional, and perhaps idealistically, simplifying things too much. But I wish to refer to the attitude of retreat from the world. I must admit that after all this attitude exists also in Christianity in the form of monachism. I am thinking here rather of one who retires from the world into the desert. Even if he goes to live in a community, he nevertheless seeks the desert as a place opposed to the world. The significance of the word "desert" has a negative aspect—that of retreat, renunciation. And curiously, the desert spirit appears as renunciation at two points: renunciation of goods—and all ascesis is here, that renunciation which goes as far as possible in reducing the "biological" claims, by fasting, for instance; and also the renunciation of family, and thus of propagation of life. It seems that here, in the family and in the fabrication and use of goods, are two roots of social life: the family society and economic society. It consequently appears that monastic life defeats social life and perhaps resolves the problem of social life in an original way by breaking, so to speak, these columns on which society and social life are supported. However this may be, there is in Christianity at attitude of retreat from the world, and, logically, one should expect this attitude to translate itself on the technological plane by a refusal. But there is no need to go into all this, it is not worth while; it is a distraction in the Pascalian sense—it distracts us from the essential matters. Obviously, we can see the extremely great spiritual force of this attitude. Even if it is true that there is a spiritual quality in technology, why should we make this detour, if it is possible to go straight to the essential, if we can go straight to God? Why should we pass through the world and through activities of the world? It is a kind of useless detour, even if it has some value. And what exactly is this value? Here I think of a phrase of Kierkegaard's: "It is a great thing to renounce one's dearest wish, but it is an even greater thing to go back on one's renunciation." He said this in reference to Abraham's sacrifice. God asks Abraham to sacrifice his son. He accepts, and then, just when he is about to sacrifice him, the angel restrains his arm. In a way, it is perhaps a finer thing for Abraham to obey God the second time than the first. It was doubtless very hard for him to give up his son, but once he had made this sacrifice, it was perhaps still harder to behave as though the sacrifice had not been necessary. So, the second sacrifice was more far-reaching than the first. It was a greater thing to return to his dearest wish when he had once renounced it. Is this not what we mean in Christianity? There is certainly the movement of withdrawal from the world expressed in the monastic vocation, but there is also the reverse movement which is a return to the world; only it is a return, a movement, which in a sense contains within itself retreat. This is expressed very well by St. Paul: "Having nothing and yet possessing everything" (II Cor. 6:10).

THE TECHNICIAN MENTALITY
AND CHRISTIANITY

Two successive religious attitudes. Finally I must come
to a conclusion. It seems to me that the problem posed to
the Christian life by the technician mentality is that of a
modification of religious attitudes—or in any case of
certain of them. To simplify, it seems to me that there have
hitherto been successively two religious attitudes and that
there is now a third taking shape. When I speak of religious
attitudes, I naturally do not look at the religious *content,*
but at the way this content is taken up in a human psychology, and lived concretely. The first model was an attitude in which man discovered himself in the presence of
the sacred, because man lived in a natural world which to
him seemed stable, given once for all, with its laws. This
nature was perceived as mysterious, as the sign and the
receptacle of the divine power, and God was conceived as
the master of nature, as the planner of the world. It was
somewhat the figure of "God, the emperor of the world,"
dominating the world and consequently dominating man
himself. Man then had only to put himself in God's hands,
committing himself to God and expecting God to give him
all he needed. A second form of the religious attitude,
which is moreover much more recent, is that of interiority,
of a return to interiority. In the first attitude, man is in a
sense open before nature; it is outside himself that he
seeks God's sign. The second attitude is the attitude in
which man seeks the presence of God and God's sign within
himself. This attitude developed just at the time when
conscience was reflecting upon itself. It was established in
a period which coincided with the discovery of the *cogito,*

of conscience, in European philosophy, a discovery which is also related to the first flight of the modern scientific spirit. Only, that interiority is in a sense an insular interiority, a conscience which discovers itself in its nakedness, in its autonomy, which sees itself as situated outside the world. We must think here of the great rationalist philosophers who tried to express just this autonomy of conscience, of thought which is only thought, and particularly of the philosophy of Spinoza, where interiority is included within a framework of pantheistic metaphysics.

The synthesis between "realism" and "idealism." But it seems to me that we are now entering upon another elaboration of the religious attitude, linked with an evolution of culture itself. This is precisely that we have discovered that conscience is not insular; in a way, we have succeeded in bringing about the synthesis between a conscience which is purely receptive in relation to external nature, and a conscience turned in upon itself, finding in itself the key to the world. We are trying in contemporary culture just to find this synthesis between what we have called "realism"—naive realism at least—and what we call "idealism," the conscience which is purely a spectator in the world, and the conscience which is origin and source of the world. And this synthesis is certainly connected with the notion of action. It is bound up with the notion of a dynamism of conscience, which is only an *openness* to the world, which is not therefore pure receptivity, and which is not creative either, but is one with the world, and one with the world in the unfolding of its own project, consequently in action in the developing of its interior potentialities, of the dynamism which dwells in it. We are trying to express the mysterious connection between the potentialities, these powers for action which we bear within us, and the potentialities that are in the world. We find a complementariness between nature and spirit. We find that there is a movement of the spirit towards nature and a movement of nature towards the spirit, and in contemporary philosophy the term dialectic—used, it is true, in all kinds of senses—is often taken to try to express, more or less, this complementariness, this circularity between spirit and nature. This new interpretation of conscience is intimately related to the development of the technical enterprise. We see very clearly the correspondence between this philosophical interpretation and the experience of technical man of himself. This new interpretation, being thus related to a new experience, will certainly give occasion for—and is already beginning to give occasion for—a new religious attitude in which it will certainly not be in the feeling of the world as sacred that man will try to find the sign of God, but rather in himself. However, it will no longer be a question of an insular and closed conscience, of a subjectivist spirituality, but of a conscience which discovers in itself the profound dynamism of action. The presence of God is to be discovered, of course, as within the soul, but it is to be discovered as the profound source of action, as the very root of this dynamism of which our undertakings each day bear witness.

The Christian hope gives its true meaning to the technical enterprise. On the other hand, what faith gives us is not only a grasp of the real nature of this dynamism but also a grasp of its true finality. I was saying just now that the project of technology is a project which remains indeterminate, whose finality remains invisible, and which consequently is somewhat formidable, even rather frightening. We do not know where it will lead us. As soon as the immanent dynamism of this project is interpreted as it may be, as it should be, from the point of view of the Christian faith, then the finality will become clearer too. Not that we shall be able—as at a spectacle—to see what is going to happen, but in this sense that we shall acquire confidence that it is leading somewhere, and that is finally to the peace of God. In other terms, it is finally Christian hope which gives its true meaning to the operation, to the technical enterprise itself.

To express all this in another way, I would say that there is a *logos* at work in the world of reason and technology, and that this *logos* exposes us to the risk of nihilism. This *logos* has a meaning for itself, but it recognizes that finally this meaning is in some measure exhausted in the very expression of it. In other words, there is in this life of the *logos* a circularity by virtue of which it may appear to itself to be totally expressed, while at the same time it discovers in this very expression that there is nothing beyond the expressing. It discovers that it is at bottom empty, that at bottom it is nothing, that this pseudo-presence of itself to itself is at bottom nothing but an absence. It is thus inhabited by a sort of nihilism. Faith and Christian hope promise man freedom from misfortune and in particular deliverance from death. But we may ask ourselves if there may not be an interpretation of this death which might be the following: "to be delivered from death" could mean "to be delivered from non-sense, from the non-sense of nihilism, from the non-sense of the *logos*." What the Christian faith reveals to us is that the work of man goes beyond itself, that it is assumable, and has in fact been assumed in a movement which surpasses it, and which links it to the very life of the totality, the life of the totality which is quite simply the very life of God.

BERNARD MOREL

Science and Technology
in God's Design

INTRODUCTION

Is there a connection between science or technology and
God's design, at least as far as this design has been defined
by the thought of the Church? Is there a connection between Holy Scripture, the source of the thought of the
traditional Church, and the contemporary scientific and
technical world? If we answer no to the question, the case
has been heard and there is no more to be said. But it is
our view that since the Church has always transmitted
Christ's message through the languages and great currents
of thought of the day, we must now give theology the
technical and scientific language suited to our age. There
is a connection which we postulate a priori between what
we call science or technology and God's design. We must
specify this connection. I want to make four introductory
remarks.

First, the determining of this connection is a particularly
ecumenical enterprise. Indeed, the confrontation of the
Church's thought with that of the contemporary world,
since it poses problems common to all confessions, enables
theologians to embark upon a field of thought which, by
its novelty and urgency, should shake certain traditional
antagonisms, and prepare the way for a collaboration which
the impasses of the classic controversies had hitherto im-
peded.

Secondly, the relations between scientific and technical thought on the one hand and theological on the other are not reversible. Science and technology can develop without the help of theological thought. On the other hand, theology is not able to borrow from current thought, whether scientific or technical, the elements which will allow it to communicate God's purpose to people of our time. This means that theology cannot be indifferent to the development of scientific thought. Not only must it try to use the language, but theology must be informed by scientific thought, even though this informing causes some modifications in certain of its classic concepts. It is not a matter of changing the nature of the deposit entrusted to the Church by the apostles, of course, but of making it yield interest by taking the evolution of thought into account.

Thirdly, this confrontation shows that between theological thought and scientific thought there is a certain contradiction, not an absolute contradiction, but elements of diversity which mean that what is axiomatic for one is not reducible to what is axiomatic for the other; at the same time, there are certain elements in common which make it impossible for theology to ignore scientific thought. This contradiction develops in practice into a dialectic wherein the opposition of the elements of identity and diversity develops according to a history on which theology par excellence could give evidence.

Fourthly and lastly, this relative diversity and identity between theology and scientific thought evokes the classic notion of analogy, which here again is still fundamental. Analogy reminds us that the difference between theological thought and scientific thought is essential, and that the identity is only in a certain respect. It is this "certain respect" which must be specified. We shall attempt this, not by an external description of the process of scientific and theological thought, but by attempting a theological formulation which takes scientific thought practically into account. It remains that the notions which we borrow from scientific thought only apply by analogy to theology, so true is it that theology cannot be a science in the strict sense of the term, since we cannot in theology give the counter-proof nor the mathematical verification of what we put forward; and this because the object of theology is the mystery of God, that is to say, God's relation to the world of his creation, and within this creation, man's relation to his Creator and his God. This mystery by definition eludes any univocal specification; the introduction or application to theology of a scientific language tends to equivocate this language out of respect for God's transcendence. So the remarks that I am going to contribute now have a personal character which, I hope, will provoke a discussion, a discussion which seems to me all the more necessary since the church I represent has not defined its position either clearly or unanimously.

SCIENCE AND TECHNOLOGY

The notion of information. We have tried to define science and technology not extensively, that is to say, from outside, but rather comprehensively, that is, from inside, by borrowing a particularly useful notion from cybernetics: the notion of information. Information is a notion which, to be thoroughly understood, would necessitate mathematical development which has no place at this meeting and of which I should be quite incapable. Let us simply recall that this notion, which is older than cybernetics

properly so-called, makes it possible to embark on problems of the philosophy of science at the point where several
specialist scientific and technical fields converge. This fact
makes it particularly useful for an encounter with theological thought.

Maxwell's demon. In order to make clear what I mean
by information, I shall use two scientific myths. First, Maxwell's demon. This is a well-known myth. Let us imagine
two containers communicating by means of a small window; in each of these containers there is the same gas. In
the container A, the gas is at a temperature of eighty degrees, and in the container B it is at forty degrees. If we
let this system formed by the containers A and B work by
itself, that is to say in the sense of the greatest probability,
at the end of a certain time, especially if the two containers
are of the same volume, we shall see the temperature
equalizing at something around forty degrees. In effect, the
rapid molecules of container A will pass into vessel B, and
the slow molecules of vessel B will pass into vessel A, so
that the mean speed of the molecules will be progressively
equalized in the two containers, and consequently the
temperature nearly the same. Following the second law of
thermodynamics, we can say that the system, in evolv-
ing towards its most probable state, has evolved towards its
state of maximum entropy, entropy here being a measure
of disorder, of anarchy, of the leveling of the structures to
which, according to the laws of statistical probability, every
physical system tends if left to itself. We shall not say more
about this notion of entropy which is in itself a very difficult notion, except to remark that information is measured in terms of negative entropy, or more accurately, that
its mathematical definition is the same as that of entropy,
but of the opposite sign. That is what we are going to show

by placing a little demon (Maxwell's demon) at the window through which the two containers communicate.

The gases in the two containers are at the same mean temperature of forty degrees. The little demon has received precise instructions: when a fast molecule in vessel B appears, the window must be shut; and conversely with vessel A: only let slow-moving molecules pass into vessel B and keep back all the fast ones. What happens? Well, we observe that the temperature of vessel A rises in proportion as that of vessel B falls. The little demon has thus diminished the entropy of the system which, at the start, was maximum: the state of the system has gradually evolved in the direction of an increasing improbability. Maxwell's demon has thus caused entropy to retreat by exercising a discriminatory action upon the evolution of the system. He has introduced what we call information into the system of negative entropy. It is by the information that he was instructed to introduce between the vessels A and B that the demon succeeded in constructing a state of minimum probability.

The myth of the stream. This is only a preliminary approach to the notion of information, which we must try now to define further, from the technical point of view, by means of a second myth, the myth of the stream. Imagine a stream rising in a high mountain and flowing through a plain into a river which will carry its waters to the sea. This stream plays a big part in the life of those who live along its banks, who count upon it to irrigate their fields, and live in dread of the floods which periodically inundate all their towns and villages. The riverains have noticed that they could not count upon a regular and fixed flow. They have tried to measure the determination of the flow, that is to say, what they could count upon,

and they have observed that the determination of the flow
did not exceed a rate of five in 3,000, the remainder measur-
ing the *rate of indetermination* or of *contingency* corre-
sponding to the hazardous variations of this flow, and consequently to the legitimate fear of the riverside inhabitants.
In order to increase the rate of determination, that is, to
diminish the rate of contingency, the riverains had the idea
of canalizing the river and installing a system of sluice-
gates and reservoirs which would protect them from catas-
trophic floods and droughts. Thus they diminished the rate
of contingency to approximately a third, in other words
they augmented the determination rate to 2,000 in 3,000.
But this is still a contingency rate too high for their safety.
What can they do? The stream is completely canalized, so
the determination rate cannot be increased. The only thing
possible is to introduce a new factor, organization, and to
diminish the contingency rate by organizing the river. The
riverside dwellers set up observation posts in various places
to watch the flow of the river, to measure threats of flood
or of drought, and to inform a central post, which takes
such decisions as will avoid catastrophes and sends messages
to the various sluice-gates so that the flow may be kept as
regular as possible. By organizing the river, that is to say,
by introducing information which they circulate throughout the system, they have succeeded in reducing the contingency rate to five in 3,000. Information here represents
the measure of order which the mind of the riverains has
introduced into the river so that, its course being properly
regulated, its dangers may be averted and its promises be
kept as far as possible.

This second example introduces us to the notion of information particularly as it is related to cybernetics. The
word cybernetics comes, of course, from the Greek meaning

pilot. Cybernetics is the art of pilotage. The information gathered at different points along the river is communicated and sorted at a central pilotage post, the brain of the system. From the control post it is then distributed to the different effective organs of the system. This example shows that information is not only a measure of order that man can introduce in order to assure his power and defend his liberty, but also a means of acting by anticipation, that is, of foreseeing phenomena which threaten danger. This action by anticipation is one of the most important aspects of cybernetics, showing that information must be included in the time of events and the duration of phenomena and not only from the point of view of abstract mathematics. It shows how experience of the past can be used to prepare the future.

A third remark: the notion of information is not peculiar to man but is a universal phenomenon found wherever there is an encounter between a living organism and its physical surroundings. It is on the frontier between animate matter and inanimate matter that it appears. When an organism perceives a variation in its surroundings, this variation represents a menace to its internal equilibrium and consequently to its life; the organism reacts at once upon itself and upon its environment in order to protect its equilibrium with its environment. Its perception, and consequently its reaction for adaptation and defence, in themselves constitute information in an elementary form. And perhaps information existed already on the infrabiological level of the heterogenesis of physical matter, where the combinations were in preparation which from large organic molecules were to make first living cells.

Man as manipulator and communicator of information. The more complex the organism, that is to say, the further it deviates from the mean, from the probable, the more information it contains. And in this respect the human species, because of the complexity of its structures, is certainly the creature which contains most information, and consequently, at least on the macroscopic scale which is ours at the present time, the most interesting creature to know and the most attractive, the most astonishing, and the one which should arouse our deepest admiration. Not only do the organisms which deviate from the statistical mean contain information, but they are also capable of it; man is certainly the greatest manipulator of information of all the animals.

It is to be noted that man is not only capable of manipulating information, but he is capable of increasing the stock and of manipulating it socially; symbolizing it by the terms of language, he can communicate it, and in this communicable state, information exists almost outside and independently of the individuals who manipulate it. The ants certainly have techniques which indicate that they have the capacity for information, but their techniques have been the same for centuries. Man, however, improves his techniques, his stock of information becomes more extensive, the experience of parents benefits the children, and human memory is not only individual but collective.

This point is extremely important, because it shows that, in the scale of organized beings, man has an absolutely unique position which has a moral significance. In fact, through the manipulations of his information, man can introduce new structures into the universe, and thus work at the evolution of this world to a state of lesser probability, but he can also, through his information, introduce disorder into the universe, un-make structures and bring certain systems back to a state of greater entropy. Thus man is revealed as both a great constructor and a great destroyer, because he has this possibility of choosing the ends he pursues and the means he employs, and consequently has also the capacity to deceive himself. The more the organism is structured, that is, of an improbable complexity, the more autonomous it also is, and this autonomy, which opens the door for him to the idea of liberty, opens it also to the idea of morals.

GOD'S PLAN

God's information and the myth of creation. Science, which is the search for and the accumulation of information, and technology, which is the manipulation of information, are not without some analogies with the first story of Genesis, the myth of creation, which we find in the first chapter of the Bible. Analogies only, for the first chapter of the Bible, like Holy Scripture as a whole, is primarily a hymn of praise from man to his Creator, whereas the search for information does not necessarily lead to the idea of a Creator. An essential difference, but nevertheless also a resemblance, and the resemblance is the following: the biblical narrative says clearly that in the beginning everything was without form and void, *tohu-vabohu* in Hebrew. This universe in chaos is the universe in a state of maximum entropy, where everything is in its most probable state of maximum disorganization, where there is neither structure, nor differentiation of levels of energy, so that not only is life impossible and there is nothing and nobody to perceive anything whatsoever, but there is not even anything to perceive; chaos represents for thought an equivalent of logical non-existence. Did God create everything out of nothing, *ex nihilo,* or out of chaos? Theologians can discuss this indefinitely; it seems to come to the same thing, and human thought cannot go further back in time beyond the idea of chaos which already represents nothingness, and to go back beyond chaos is to go beyond the imaginable.

In the beginning God said, "Let there be light, and there was light." God spoke and it was so. God created by means of his word. The word is here the analogy of the information about which we have just been talking. God introducing information into the universe in chaos created structures, developed a process which from structures to more complex structures led the universe of chaos by ways of physical and biological evolution through to man, the most heterogenized creature. The entropy of the universe decreased in proportion as God's information was introduced into chaos; and this entropy became least in man at the climax of biological evolution, the creature through whom God crowned his creative work on the sixth day. The six days of creation have evidently no common term with our universe's billions of years. But in this poetic summary we discover an intuition of the direction of evolution. Starting with light, the first fundamental structuration of chaos, God's information leads evolution towards its at present most perfect term—man.

Thus the very notion of information helps us to understand better theologically the intention of God, who in creating the whole universe by his word sought to give himself a vis-à-vis to whom he could talk and who would consequently answer him, a responsible vis-à-vis who, discovering in his turn all the riches of creation, would discern the plan of the Creator in order to submit himself to it. Perhaps it is through his capacity for information that man is in the image and likeness of God; indeed it is through his information that man can respond to his Creator as a child to his father, and that he can intervene in the world in a manner which has something of the creative quality. Man is certainly incapable of producing structures out of nothing, but at least he can intervene in processes in such a way as to make them evolve towards a less probable state which may be more to the glory of God, and thus, through his science and his technology, make all creation sing the praise of its Creator.

Human information has religious significance. It seems throughout the biblical myths of Genesis that this was God's plan. Man is not put upon earth simply in order to go on living, but in order to extend his power. The names which man was to give to all the creatures which God made to pass before him, according to the text of the second chapter of Genesis, would be preserved not only in men's memory, but in God's. Human achievement is thus a sign of God's action in the world. Human information, or more accurately, the symbols through which this information is elaborated and communicated, have a religious significance. God takes human science and technology into account. He attaches a divine value to them in proportion as man is in his own image and likeness. It is in conformity with God's plan that man should seek to know all the secrets of the universe in which he is called to live and to increase his power, and that in this should essentially consist his responsibility towards the Creator. In as far as he uses his information intelligently, to create new structures in God's universe, he responds to his vocation as a man and collaborates (if that term is not presumptuous) in the creative work of God, in whose image and likeness he "scientifically and technically" is made. Freedom is in a certain fashion the corollary of power. God, when he created man capable of information, conferred upon him an autonomy of a special kind which we call freedom, because it is in the ultimate analysis mysterious in the image and likeness of the mystery of God's freedom: something in man irreducible to determinist laws, and in which both the dignity and the responsibility of the child of God are manifest.

THE FALL AND REDEMPTION

The fall resulted from the misuse of liberty. The third chapter of Genesis reminds us of an unfortunately obvious fact. Man has not used his liberty with the sole object of glorifying God; he has manipulated for his interest the information which he has mastered. This is not the place to develop this classic chapter of theology on the origins of sin. Man ought to use his information to manifest by intelligent co-operation his submission to God the Creator; and man has not done so, or at least he has not always done so. Henceforth all the manipulations of information indicate, all at once and contradictorily, that man was created in the image and likeness of God, and so far his information is in conformity with God's plan; but on the other hand, he manipulates this information in what we will schematically call egoistic interests, and so it is no longer in conformity with God's plan. Instead of collaborating with the universal heterogenesis which leads the world of chaos to the repose of the seventh day, he contributes to the universal homogenesis which leads the creation of the sixth day back to the original chaos.

Universal heterogenesis started out from chaos and ended with man, and now this special form of homogenesis which we call sin starts with man at the climax of the evolution of life, and returns through the whole creation to the chaos which is the end of the world, according to the laws of statistical probability (a generalization from the second principle of thermodynamics), which man aggravates by his misuse of liberty. I shall not give an example: they come to mind only too easily.

It is not only man's relations with his physical environment which are thus disturbed, but also his relations with his fellows. Mishandling his information, he does himself and others injury, and this suffering which he endures or causes is a sign that by his sin he hastens his own destruction, confirming in some sort these words of Scripture: "The wages of sin is death."

Thus he tends to bring both himself and his neighbor back to the chaos from which he has been led. If, to speak metaphorically, "the grain of dust" is at the origin of human life, it is also at the end of man's existence. The grain of dust is the origin of human life, but not of the individual's life, for he was born of his parents and developed from a living cell. On the other hand, dust is the end of the life of every individual, but not of the human species, which by reproduction pursues its way towards the seventh day of creation. From now on this progress is accompanied by a feeling of bad conscience: man is divided between his sense of power and his desire to use it for generous and useful purposes, and his sense of inadequacy, incapable as he is of avoiding temptations to egoism, that is, to selfish power. The struggle to live, inevitable wars and bloodshed, have a meaning in terms of good and evil which scriptural revelation transposes into terms of sin.

The relation between God and man is also affected by this misuse of liberty. Whereas between God and man these relationships should be harmonious, they are now dialectical. An element of contradiction has entered in, just as man's good will comes into conflict with his evil will; the love of the father watching over his child's happiness becomes the irritation of the judge who cannot endure the sin of his creature. The image of Adam and Eve driven out of the garden of Eden shows how God's curse weighs upon the manipulations of human information. Henceforth man has no longer a simple relationship with his Creator; the disturbance introduced by sin shows itself dialectically in human information which is at once a sign of God's blessing and a sign of his curse upon man and his activities.

Redemption through Christ, the alpha and omega of creation. The Bible from end to end shows that God does not abandon man who breaks with him; he comes to meet his child to rescue him from the consequences of his error. This story of God who goes to meet men is told prophetically in the Old Testament and historically in the New. Christ, the Son of God, comes to reforge the link broken by sin.

There is a divine dialectic of immanence and transcendence: immanence, the force through which God approaches his creation, establishes himself in her, becomes incarnate in the person of the Son, and makes himself present to the world, and transcendence, which is the contrary force whereby God, judge and saint, withdraws from men, abandons them to their sins and to death, leaving them to return to chaos. This dialectic attains its highest point of contradiction in the mystery of Christ, in which the forces of immanence and transcendence oppose each other to the point where God becomes man while remaining God, the All Other in the humanity of Christ. The dogma of the "two natures" defined by the Fathers of Chalcedon admirably illustrates this contradiction: the person of the Son is incarnate in human nature in such a way that in Christ the divine and human natures are closely conjoined but not confused. They are united "without separation or division," but also, according to the famous formulation of the Chalcedon definition, "without confusion or mixture"; the divine nature is at once immanent and transcendent in human nature.

Christ is the mystery who counteracts the fall and restores to man the possibility of reunion with God and collaboration with the work of creation, because he is, supremely, the crown of creation; he actualizes perfectly "the image and likeness of God" in which and for which man was created.

He is the alpha of creation because he is the Word of God, that is, he is the Information through which God brought the world out of chaos; he is also the omega of creation because he actualizes the perfection for which God has created all things and set man at the head of his creation. His cross, on the other hand, shows that he knows death, not only as the sign of God's judgment, but also as a way to eternal life. When he rose again, he delivered, through man whose nature he had assumed, the whole creation from the fatality of death. If God created life, it was not so that death should carry it away for good. The dialectic between life and death at the end of the universal heterogenesis and homogenesis in which it seemed that the destiny of man was confined, this dialectic was firmly inflected in the direction of the triumph of life. Therefore the alpha and omega of creation, in the heart of human history, accomplished everything; his earthly work and existence remain the supreme evidence.

SCIENCE AND TECHNOLOGY
AND THE PERSON OF CHRIST

The reconciliation of science and technology with God.
Christ is not only a historical person whose individuality is
confined to one human place and time. As he himself
promised his apostles, he remains alive throughout the
history of man through the presence of his Spirit; or, more
accurately, through the Holy Spirit he himself remains
present with men until the last day when, by his coming
again, he will complete their history. Thus he is the perpetual mystery of human history, living in his Church
which in some sense is itself Christ, living in the inner
life of the faithful who through their spiritual life are also
in a sense Christ, living everywhere in the world where
men struggle and hope, and gathering the whole of humanity into the humanity of his existence. Today Christ, in
his two natures as defined at Chalcedon, still reconciles
humanity with God, and in this humanity are comprised
all the values which have composed it through the ages,
in this instance the science and technology of our epoch.

All that human information stands for is assumed in
this mystery of Christ's humanity; modern science and
technology were already present in Christ dying on the
cross, and are therefore reconciled with God. Of course,
scientists and technicians remain sinners in their manipulation of information, but this sin does not deface science
with shadows that will cast a veil of pessimism over its future. If Christ has truly reconciled men with God, and if
he is himself humanity in its completion, Christ will at the
end of history be the conclusion of all this human search
which today we call scientific. He is the omega, not only
of God's creation, but also of the hope which men try to

make real by their scientific and technical work. The dialectic of sin continues, but the grace of God will triumph over man's sin. The technician and the scientist may still be divided today between their desire to follow God's design and the temptation to follow their own ambitious designs, but they know that a hope has been extended to them that nothing and nobody, no power in this world, can destroy: the victory in the end of the Creator, through Christ, over all that could deflect creation from its purpose, which is God's peace.

The eschatological significance of scientific research. This optimism has thus a fundamentally eschatological significance. Neither today nor tomorrow will man know how to handle his information in a way truly conformed to his vocation as a child of God; he will contrive to make mistakes, to destroy his environment, to wound his neighbor, perhaps even to kill himself. But if we look beyond the horizons of our mathematical foresight into the mystery of God's promise, we should face the future with confidence: not only is God stronger than all the dynamisms which cause us to break with him, but in man's technical and scientific effort he finds collaboration of a kind which makes a decisive contribution to the completion of his creative work. Therefore, if we really believe in Christ, we must believe that nothing in the world, even in the heart of man, can compromise the plan which God has had for all eternity.

There is a dialectic between man's collaboration and non-collaboration with God which still remains, for it is certain that the scholar pushing his scientific research is not necessarily aware that he is working at God's creation. Science, as we said at the beginning, develops independently of the faith of the believer and of the theology of the Church. But the Christian scholar has this advantage over the non-Christian scholar, that he knows not only what he is doing in the immediate present but also in relation to the most distant future. He knows that in spite of the forces of selfishness which continue to be at work in the intentions of his will, he will yet be a real fellow-laborer if he trusts God to fight his spiritual battles with him.

He is very often obliged to take part in the works of destruction which men cannot help producing. But through all the manifestations of violence, of war, in short, of destruction, in spite of all these forces that men unleash so that death remains their most cruel menace, he knows that Christ is the omega of his research.

More than ever, in the confrontation of science with theological thought, the mystery of Christ as defined at Chalcedon is fundamental. He is the foundation of the hope of scientific research and its technical applications, provided that the eschatological bearing of the Chalcedon definitions is underlined. The Christ to whom we look is not only a man who lived nearly two thousand years ago; he is the Mystery of God, who comes from the end of time to meet man's hope and his scientific and technical research, so that this research may be a sign of Christ's second coming, and take up the universal praise of creation, passing from this world of tensions, struggles, and conflicts into the peace of the seventh day: God's peace, man's peace, and the peace of all creation.

FRANÇOIS RUSSO, S.J.

Modern Science
and the Christian Faith

IT IS no new thing for Christians to look at the development of science and consider its religious repercussions. In
the beginning the questions were limited in range and concerned the origin of the universe and of man, particularly
the interpretation of Genesis, and more recently the origin
of life and evolution.

These questions have not lost their urgency, but we tend
to look at them today more broadly and more searchingly
than in the past: what comes to the fore in the science-faith
debate is no longer so much the particular problems themselves, as the whole question of the destiny of science and
its place in human existence and consciousness. Ultimately
it is this global and more fundamental question which
poses the more serious problems for our faith. We shall try
here to look at the major aspects of this problem.

For this purpose, before we deal directly with the relationship between science and faith, we need to draw a
broad outline of modern scientific research. For we have
not as yet measured all its dynamism and significance.

THE PURPOSE OF SCIENTIFIC RESEARCH

In its intentions and in its methods, science is beginning
to show increasingly *definite* characteristics, which we are
being rather slow to recognize.

Science—the search for truth. Science has always been an attempt to reach the truth about matter, but in modern science this pursuit of truth appears in a guise which is in many respects new, and which makes a deep impression on our civilization.

Science as we know it today appears to be increasingly based on a *love of research.* By this we mean that the ideal of the scientist today is not so much the attainment and contemplation of truth as progress towards it, the strain of the whole being to achieve it. This change of perspective must be attributed in large measure to the fact that, whereas in the past one could believe that the truth about matter was accessible to whoever sought it, today it appears increasingly to be attainable only at the cost of an effort which is at the limit of human capacity.

It is impossible to over-stress this characteristic of modern science. Whether it is a matter of theoretical problems or of experimental techniques, nature yields up her secrets less and less easily. Immense efforts are made today to elaborate a satisfactory theory of the behavior of the nucleus and of the nature of the elementary particles which compose it, or again, to elucidate the physics of solids; in the experimental field enormous sums of money have been spent on the construction of great accelerators like that at CERN, in Geneva, in order to make an advance in the study of high-energy physics. How difficult it appears to be to get further light on the inner mechanism of life: what immense work is being done at the present time on the physical chemistry of the nucleus of the cell.

Sometimes we even wonder if we have not reached the limits of possible investigation, if some knowledge is not forever inaccessible. In the field of astronomy especially this impression would seem to be inescapable. But we must not give in too soon; moreover, man—or rather, mankind, for there is no question of an individual science today—is not ready to give in. The passion for knowledge is too strong to allow science to halt in the face of difficulties. Thus in spite of serious set-backs, we do not hesitate to devote powerful resources to the mastery of nuclear energy and the fusion of light elements, which we have only achieved so far in the more than brutal form of the H-bomb.

I think we are not betraying the secret intention of the scientist, or, to put it more strongly, the passion which animates him, if we see in it a response to a call inscribed in man's inmost self, urging him to "reveal" the truth about matter. Jean Ladrière expressed this admirably in an article on the meaning of scientific research (*Lumen Vitae*, 1960, no. 3), which I may perhaps be allowed to summarize:

"If science remains still to be accomplished it is because the logos of the world still remains a hidden logos. The revelation of it is barely beginning, and it is man's privilege to bring it about. We are face to face with one of man's fundamental responsibilities in relation to the world, of a dimension of his vocation which he is only just beginning to recognize. Certainly, man is not a creator in the full and direct meaning of the term. In this undertaking he finds himself presented with a datum. But this is a *hidden* datum. It must be explicated, brought out into the daylight. Science is precisely this—this process through which the world as nature finds its fulfilment and its apotheosis in the world as logos."

We have to reach this stage if we want to measure exactly what the scientific ideal stands for today. At this point science no longer appears as a minor or optional form of occupation on a par with a number of others. It appears as a *vital* activity which man cannot do without, any more than he can do without bread. It constitutes a task in which man possesses himself, frees himself, and knows himself, for the reason which we have just given, that it is his deepest vocation.

These few indications will, we hope, have helped us to understand the full seriousness and gravity which characterize the contemporary scientific task. Science becomes less and less an amusement, a distraction, a hobby, as it often was in the past. It appears increasingly to be a task from which man cannot escape, even apart from any useful results. More than ever, we can take as our maxim, "It is imperative that science should be." Does someone ask the scientist, why? The scientist is rarely a philosopher and will no doubt find it difficult to explain himself on this subject. But let there be no misunderstanding—as there sometimes is: the scientist's lack of skill in defining his ideal is in no way a sign that he lacks one, or is not devoted to it. On the contrary, it is because the dynamism of science is at the deepest level of the consciousness of contemporary man that it is so difficult to put it into words.

Now this design of scientific knowledge whose force and seriousness we have been discussing, is not the concern of a few as in the past. An ever-increasing section of humanity is becoming involved.

Pure scientific research, *basic research* which is not concerned with applying knowledge, has already assumed very large proportions, and requires not only scientists in the old sense of great creative minds, but scientific assistants and also technicians of various degrees of skill.

But beyond pure science, scientific truth makes itself known in our civilization through *technology.* The latter, indeed, should not be considered only as the pursuit of efficaciousness, of a useful result. It is also an *illustration of the truth of science* to the ever-increasing extent that it is applied science, science set to work.

Finally, thanks to *popular science,* which is constantly improving in quality and appealing to an ever-wider public, the scientific ideal is gaining ground, outside the world of scientists and technicians, among the mass of the population.

It is therefore no exaggeration to say that our civilization lives in a scientific atmosphere.

Science as an attitude of mind. We do not intend to give a detailed account of the scientific attitude. This analysis has, in any case, frequently been made. But what we essentially intend to do is something less often done, to emphasize how far this attitude of mind is *determined,* and this is new in many respects, in relation to the old ways of approaching positive reality, and *differentiated* from the philosophical and religious attitudes from which it was not until recently clearly distinguished.

It is important also to ask on what grounds the scientific method can justify itself. Truth to tell, these have hitherto been rather thin on the speculative plane; science was primarily justified by its success. In other terms, science has furnished its proofs rather than justified itself, properly speaking. This state of affairs is not without its consequences.

On the strength of its success, science has tended to claim

sometimes rather exaggerated virtues for the scientific method. For lack of sufficient consideration of the cause and even of the nature of its successes, many men of today have come to think that science can solve all problems, or even that it offers the only valid approach.

THE PLACE OF SCIENCE IN LIFE AND THOUGHT

It is of supreme importance that the scientific enterprise outlined above should be seen in its place among man's activities as a whole, and especially its relationship to religious life and thought. This is an urgent question which has not hitherto been undertaken with the seriousness and attention which it requires. Some tend to deny science the place which is its right: heirs to a narrowly conceived classical humanism, "literary gentlemen" indifferent to scientific values, and sometimes, let us face it, theologians who are disquieted by the growth of science which they see as the enemy of faith. Others take the opposite view and tend to give so much importance to science that no room, or not enough, is left for other activities of the spirit.

We must go beyond these inaccurate views and fruitless comparisons—which is possible, especially if we recognize that a relatively new form of mental life is tending to assert itself: situations or distinctions, or, on the other hand, too simple harmonizations of mental attitudes are being superseded by a state of differentiation, in which we shall have to accept tensions which may be slightly uncomfortable but will be ultimately beneficial, and will lead to the purification and widening of perspective that facilitate possibly less easy but ultimately more fruitful and accurate syntheses.

If we limit ourselves to the problem of the relative position of science and faith, we find the following principal points of view in which science and faith appear in duality, and to a certain extent in tension.

We must tackle them honestly, as definitely as possible, bringing all available light to bear upon them. We must not be content any longer with the vagueness, uncertainty, and plausibility which we have "made do with" for so long.

1. Whereas the truth of faith dominates time (is truth, truth definitively acquired), if not in all its developments yet at least in its essential affirmation, scientific truth is a *progressive truth* which is ceaselessly correcting and completing itself. Faith and science are each right in their own order. But it will be understood that, in a world where the ideal of such a progressive scientific truth is increasingly accepted, it is perhaps fitting that we should take more trouble than in the past to justify the invariable character of the truth of faith. I do not intend to produce this proof here; I only go so far as to state the problem and to observe that, whereas the scientist needs to be very careful not to claim that progressive truth is the only truth accessible to man and worthy of his intellect, the theologian on his side must beware of so presenting faith that the pursuit of progressive truth by the scientific method appears to be an occupation without meaning or importance.

2. Science is interested primarily in matter, in things. Even when it concerns itself with man, it does not penetrate his subjectivity, his essential being, but only to the point where he is open to analysis as a *positive reality*. Furthermore, the interest of science aims at the *detail* of matter. Science certainly is not without regard for syn-

thesis, but this synthesis could only be valid for it if all the details were included and integrated.

This is not the primary aim of religious truth, which enlightens us first about our destiny and the meaning of our existence. For this reason the Christian revelation did not need to wait for the theory of relativity nor for quantum mechanics.

There is a duality of aim here which, of course, is not ultimately a contradiction, but which nevertheless deserves to be taken seriously. For unless we take care, the men of our day, penetrated with the scientific spirit, will soon be regarding the purely objective and *detailed* knowledge offered by science as sufficient for the understanding of man and of the world, all other interpretations being consigned to the category of childish and mythical explanations which belong to a bygone age.

Here again we must be on our guard, both against the facile views of certain scientists for whom the almighty power of scientific understanding is unquestioned, and against certain Christian thinkers who withhold the respect that is due to this objective and detailed study of matter.

We have not satisfactorily resolved the confrontation of the truth of faith and the truth of science when we have exposed the partial and incomplete nature of science's positive explanation. We must produce other views which will underline the legitimacy, the dignity, and the necessity of such positive knowledge, from the very standpoint of that conception of man proposed by faith.

In particular, Christian scientists must overcome this tendency to a bad conscience which too many non-scientists enjoy maintaining in them, a tendency which comes from the fear of leaving man and his faith behind when they begin to take an interest in matter, and still more when, as specialists, they devote the geater part of their energies to a narrow section of positive reality.

Certainly, in such work their sense of the human, their religious sense, may be in danger of deterioration; but fundamentally this is not an inhuman position in which they find themselves, for in engaging upon it they are fulfilling their human vocation.

3. We now tackle a more radical aspect of the duality of science and faith, that presented by the ever-sharper neutrality and autonomy of the scientific enterprise. The further science progresses, the more it is concerned to protect itself from all compromise, to purify itself from foreign elements which might intrude into its procedure, and especially from the themes and arguments deriving from philosophy and from theology. These foreign elements may encumber it, impede its effort, and even put it onto the wrong track, as the history of science demonstrates.

The scientist of today is extremely susceptible on this point. He has increasing difficulty in bearing with the syncretism which particularly rejoiced the learned men of the seventeenth century, Newton or Descartes, for instance, to quote only the very great ones, who brought in the hand of God at every verse end.

Again let us repeat, with an emphasis for which we apologize, but which seems appropriate if we are to reach the most obstinate minds, that if this state of affairs does not in itself constitute an obstacle to faith, it is nevertheless true that it cannot fail to raise a problem, at least psychologically.

One must be honest enough to recognize that among Christians who are alive to the possible effect upon their

faith of the development in themselves of a scientific mentality, there is a disquiet which is due to the lack of any
apparent connection between science and religious matters, to the desacralization of the world resulting from the
spread and growing prestige of the scientific explanation.

Can we say that "classic" religious teaching has a satisfactory answer to this difficulty? That is not certain. Too
often it seems to us to beg the question, to answer it super-
ficially, for lack of having really faced it in all its implications.

In a world increasingly penetrated by this "neutralist"
spirit, we cannot be satisfied with appealing to the in-
dubitably essential distinction between the orders of
knowledge. This distinction is not as simple as it is often
said to be. It must be made clear in a sufficiently expanded
and profound argument that, on the one hand, this attitude of neutrality is "methodologically" necessary and of
the highest importance for reaching the positive truth
about matter, and that it only attacks a "sacralization" of
the world which ultimately is not essential to faith, but
that, on the other hand, it only constitutes a "moment" in
the complete knowledge of reality. A full understanding
of man and of the world must be broader and deeper and
go beyond scientific thought, and neutrality must be abandoned without any suggestion of an abdication of the intellect in the highest and most authentic sense of the word.

In such an analysis we must beware of certain facile
purisms which are to be met in the camp both of the
philosophers and of the scientists. It is here that a work
like that of Père Teilhard de Chardin finds its meaning
and its justification. In spite of certain debatable philosophical opinions, he was a scientist completely familiar
with the positive method, who yet sought to go beyond the

neutrality of pure scientific knowledge, demonstrating admirably how in the heart of science itself there can be heard a call to go further.

If we were unable thus to indicate the place and importance of scientific effort, we should see faith giving way before a domination of the scientific spirit which would soon become a religion. Do we not see this happening today in certain circles, where a curious landslide makes this scientific neutrality become the basis of a new faith, and claim to constitute in itself a complete vision of the world and its destiny? A global elite of men trained by science and technology may well come to believe that, concretely, only the progress of science can answer the questions, religious ways having only a secondary importance henceforth. Religion could still be respected, even esteemed, under these conditions, but only as a consolation, as something that feeds the affections, and no longer as the light and guide of existence.

Going deeper into the modern scientific attitude, we find it dominated by a *rationalist* hope of a perhaps hitherto unmeasured dimension. This hope is for an entire mastery of truth, a total reconstruction of the world by the human spirit. A certain kind of rationality, of a vigor and intensity never attained hitherto, tends to pass into everybody's life, to become a live formula for existence. Present-day science may be far from this ideal, but let us make no mistake about it, its soul and driving-force are here.

We need not dwell at length on the consequences of this attitude for the life of faith, which could never be satisfied with the evidence of reason alone.

Once again, faced with this situation, we must beware of facile solutions, but we must not be disturbed. Let us see in this state of affairs an invitation to make a better presentation of the exact nature of faith: faith does not despise reason, but faith has good reasons for presenting man with wider horizons beyond strictly scientific rationality.

We should need to extend these analyses if we wished to present a complete view of the contemporary duality of science and of faith and of the harmonizations called for. But the three views which we have looked at will have sufficed, we think, to show—and this was our essential objective—that the confrontation of faith and science cannot be treated lightly, and requires notably an exact understanding of the nature of the scientific objective.

We are certainly faced with a difficult and delicate question, which can only be answered with a very serious effort.

It is possible that many of those who encounter the scientific mentality, whether they are involved directly or indirectly in scientific work, particularly if they are responsible for bringing the Christian message into circles influenced by science, have not yet seen sufficiently clearly all that must be conscientiously *overcome* so that the full *openness* of mind which is a condition for the acceptance of faith shall be safeguarded or rediscovered, an openness which in many respects science is in danger of compromising.

This task—all that has just been said will have sufficed, we hope, to make this understood—is not only a matter of defense, and does not consist only of putting people on their guard; we must more positively set before the Christian of today an *equilibrium* of the life of the spirit which will be new in this sense, that it must include an acceptance without reserve and without timidity of the scientific attitude, however much it may at first sight appear to be opposed to the attitude of faith. This acceptance, though it certainly implies an ordeal, will be ultimately beneficial for faith, precisely because it will have imposed this ordeal. But to operate in the direction willed by God, this acceptance must include the condition of clearly setting out the exact possibilities of the scientific method, which could not claim to contribute all the truth, nor constitute the only valid behavior of the mind.

Contemporary man sees himself finally invited to an intellectual "way of being" more differentiated than in the past. Far from seeing a danger for faith in this new situation, we see, on the contrary, the possibility of a purer, more personal, more courageously and fully adopted, faith.

JEAN DE LA CROIX KAELIN, O.P.

Faith and Technology

THE thoughts which follow are an attempt to define, from the Roman Catholic point of view, the Christian attitude to the technological revolution of the modern world. When I say "the Christian attitude," I am not thinking of the attitude which Christians have in fact taken. We are all well enough aware of the oft-deplored divorce between a certain so-called Christian mentality and the post-Renaissance scientific mentality. I shall therefore waste no time over that. What interests me is the Christian attitude as it issues from the vision of man given us by the Catholic faith, a vision which bears not only on the essence, but on the existential situation, of redeemed man in the world.

I

MAN'S DOUBLE FINALITY

Man receives a twofold call from God. The one, which proceeds from his very nature, consists of filling the earth and subduing it and having dominion over every living thing. The other, which proceeds from grace, makes him a son of God and brings him into intimate relationship with the Divine Persons, sets him on the path towards an objective which is nothing less than perfect communion in the very life of God for eternity.

This does not mean that man's life will be in two parts.

Man must live his life-in-the-world as a son, not merely as the servant who does not share his Master's purpose, who does not work for himself, but as the son and the friend, who enters into his Father's plans, and whose work forms part of a whole from which he is not excluded. This communion in the divine will for earthly existence presupposes communion in the divine will concerning the actual mystery of the Deity. It is through the same theological love that man consents to what God is in himself, beyond all created things—hallowed be thy name—and that he consents and strives that the divine will shall be done on earth as it is in heaven.

The love which is charity, agape, guarantees the unity of man in the diversity of his tasks and of his twofold vocation.[1]

---

[1] We find the same thought in a remarkable study by Professor Jean Ladrière, "History and Destiny," in the *Revue philosophique de Louvain*, February, 1960. "The notion of destiny carries with it the suggestion of finality and at the same time of a call, and also this idea that man cannot accede to the truth of his own being except inasmuch as he allows himself to be carried away by this call. But this call may be, as it were, the very word of what is truly human in man, what makes him a man, or it may be a call from God revealing himself to man. We must, therefore, make a distinction between natural and supernatural destiny. In the first, the initiative is with reason, the foundation course of human nature. In the second, the initiative is with God, and in relation to the former it represents an overplus, a bonus which no natural disposition, no merit of his own, could procure for man; in a word, it is a completely free gift.

"This definition, however, cannot be taken as signifying mere juxtaposition. From the moment when supernatural destiny enters in, it produces its effects not only within its own order, but also within the natural order; without modifying what is essential to this order it exercises an influence which rectifies and activates its powers. Thus one may speak, as Maritain does, of a secondary effect of grace which is a superelevation of nature within its own order. Thus we see charity quickening civic friendship, fortifying the spirit of peace and unity—or faith lending reason a reflection of its own light, in reason's activity of philosophy."

SIN AND REDEMPTIVE GRACE

The rupture caused by sin, and which could have completely compromised the divine plan, has not in fact done so. The grace of redemption succeeds the grace of innocence. Man the sinner is still the man called to build the earthly city and the City of God. Through the grace of Christ he can respond to this call. Faith and baptism bring him into the fellowship of the Father, the Son, and the Holy Spirit, and allow him to work in the world as a son of God.

But interior unity is only given in embryo, in a nature which the rupture somehow upset and delivered up to anarchy. Even when reconciled, man must still struggle to subdue the totality of his being to the law of unitive love.

It is from day to day that "the inner man" (II Cor. 4:16) must be renewed. The dynamics of the supernatural life, if not thwarted, make of the baptized new creatures who, "with unveiled face, beholding the glory of the Lord, are being changed into his likeness from one degree of glory to another; for this comes from the Lord who is the Spirit" (II Cor. 3:18). At the climax of this transformation through which the Christian reflects more and more brightly the image of Christ, who is the perfect "image of the invisible God" (Col. 1:15), anarchy would be overcome, and the Christian made perfect as the Heavenly Father is perfect, partaking of that very unity of the three Divine Persons.

THE COSMOS

The world of nature, the physical universe, proceeded from God's creative power. "God saw everything that he had made, and behold, it was very good" (Gen. 1:31). Created for man, who himself was created for God, the universe is affected in some manner by the vicissitudes of man's spiritual adventure. But the universe is not affected by man's sin and by Christ's redemption in the same manner. The hope of glory, due to Christ's resurrection, is for the universe of the senses the promise of a new state, achieved in ways beyond our power to imagine, but certainly conferring on it a beauty and a splendor derived not from material sources but from the supernatural glory of the Spirit. "The subjection to futility" of which St. Paul speaks (Rom. 8:20) does not imply that the material creation has become bad in itself whereas it was once good. The curse which was put upon it after the fall—"Cursed is the ground because of you" (Gen. 3:17), said Yahweh to Adam—in no way justifies such a Manichaean interpretation. Whereas divine hope really makes the whole universe share in the expectation of the Parousia wherein its own laws will be found to have changed, perhaps somewhat like those of risen bodies, man's sin cannot make the cosmos intrinsically bad. What then is the meaning of the curse of Genesis? Nothing more nor less than this: it is enough that the heart of man should change, for its relation to the universe to be upset, and for the latter to become not only a place of exile, but also a vale of tears, and from some points of view a snare and a temptation. In the Christian experience of a life regarded as a period of exile and testing, there is nothing which in itself justifies contempt for the world, nothing to prevent one enjoying this marvelous world of nature. The primitive command that man should subdue the earth and dominate every other living thing has not been rescinded. Only the conditions of its performance have altered, and the brittleness of a will which can resist grace has made the effort of this will ambiguous when applied to the construction of the world, just as its successes are ambiguous, being usable for good or evil.

We shall show how there can co-exist in the Christian, without any contradiction, both a wonder-filled vision of nature, of this nature that he is also called to mark with his seal, to transform for the service and delight of mankind, and also his keen consciousness of the precariousness of things here below and the misery of the human condition.

TECHNOLOGY

On condition that we keep the preceding considerations in mind, we may embark upon the problem of technology itself.

It is part of the call received by man by virtue of his very nature. Every creature, indeed, whether spiritual or material, is subjected to the law of development. Man, who stands at the horizon of purely spiritual realities and of the cosmos, not by virtue of juxtaposing these two separate worlds within himself but by making them meet in the substantial unity of his being, does not escape this law. To develop is to bring to their completion the inherent capacities of his nature. If he is ordered to subdue the earth, it is not only because the earth is intended to increase its fertility with the help of man's labor, but it is also and primarily because man will develop himself in this encounter which, on account of sin, has become a struggle.

Technological activity, like social life, is one of the consequences of man's condition as spirit incarnate. So we see it at the dawn of history, as the first sign which helps us to recognize a kinsman. For, essentially, it is the introduction into material reality of a finality proper to man.[2] From this

[2] Cf. "Valeur humaine de la technique," in *Nova et Vetera* (Fribourg, 1950), 1, 1-23.

it derives an intrinsic value which, like the work of art, is to be a witness to our dignity, a sign, written in stone or other material, of freedom and the spirit. It carries a surplus-value of being. And this surplus helps to form our actual state, by liberating it from physical and biological servitudes. Without technology, whether that whereby man succeeded for the first time in preserving the flame after a fire caused by lightning, or produced by rubbing two flints together, whether it was printing or the steam engine, we should not be what we are. Already automation is transforming life enormously, and the development of cybernetics and its applications will doubtless considerably modify the features of our society.

Technology itself is a good, and so therefore is the science which makes it possible and which in turn benefits from it. It is not moral goodness, which belongs to another order, that of freedom, but it is what philosophers and theologians call ontological goodness.

It would follow that the ontological goodness of which we are speaking, and whose corollary is the notion of integrity, would intrinsically imply a certain finality, this reference to the use which man is called to make of it. If we imagine, for example, a machine or some object which is remarkable for technical achievement, but the use of which could not be anything but immoral, whose very existence would tempt to sin, we could perhaps say that something essential is missing which would enable this object fully to epress this notion of ontological goodness, as though it reflected the morality—or immorality—of its author. "Every instrument carries within itself," said Heisenberg, "the spirit in which it was created." [3] In fact, this finality of the object is independent of its author's

[3] *Physique et Philosophie* (Paris, 1961), p. 10.

purposes for himself. The author gives the object its human or anti-human finality. He gives it its own special purpose. The technical object is morally neutral. Only the use to which it is put is susceptible of a moral qualification.

But to recognize this intrinsic goodness of all true knowledge, of every discovery, of every valid technical achievement, is not without significance from the point of view of man and his freedom of action. The immoral use of visible creation, and this derived creation which is technical achievement, is certainly an offence against God in the first place—a refusal to take this place as a son of God in the world, to perform in it the work willed by the Father —but it is also to deflect a good thing from the purposes which gave it all its meaning when they inserted it in some way into what we might call the hymn of creation. The bad use to which technology may be put remains accidental to it and does not detract from the benefit which it represents as a liberating factor for man.

Again from the ontological point of view, we could underline a fortunate consequence of technology. It is one of the signs of men's solidarity. Whatever I do today, I am in debt to the research, the effort, and the work of unknown brothers.

From what has just been said, it might be concluded that sin has not tainted the cultural achievement of which technology is one aspect. The sinner himself—in the Catholic sense, the man who wittingly lives cut off from God and who wholly or in part refuses the grace of redemption (even if he preserves supernatural faith and hope)— the sinner himself can make something technically perfect, for example a hearing aid for the deaf. This work is good and remains good. It helps to build the earthly city, to push back the limits of real servitude. Yet the author, even if he was not moved by evil motives in making it (it is not impossible that he should have had the explicit purpose of serving his brethren), did not for all that act as a son of God, in this close union with God which alone is the basis of charity. His work and the perfection of his accomplishment do not advance him one step nearer salvation, which transcends all human achievement. At most, by maintaining a certain natural generosity within him, they remove some supplementary obstacle (instead of working he might be an opium addict!) and somewhat diminish the difficulties of a Christian standard of behavior when the grace of conversion has been accepted.

II

THE END AND THE MEANS

We were saying that although sin has not spoiled what was ontologically good, nor nullified the command given to man to subdue the earth and cultivate the garden of creation, man redeemed by grace remains a morally frail creature. Christ's victory in him does not protect him right away from the temptations of evil. Without prejudging the heart's secrets, it seems possible to say without risk of error that on the whole man tends to use the gifts of nature and the gifts of grace badly rather than well. It is undoubtedly the same with the gifts of technology. Such a consideration only applies, it is true, to one aspect. It is when we compare man in his dignity as a person and in relation to his essential vocation with the actual behavior which he chooses most of the time that sadness grips the heart.

Perhaps the wisdom of the Far East has turned away from technical activity and the things of this world partly because of this bitter experience. Whatever the metaphysical presuppositions which support it, moreover, we know that it is more guided in its deeper choices by a grasp which it owes to experience of the slavery of the spirit imprisoned by the cosmic illusion, than by the rational principles which serve to explain its views and discursively justify its alarms.

The attitude of the East cannot fail to awaken a responsive echo in the Christian. For after all, the eye of faith increases the dignity of man to infinity; the affirmation of absolute transcendence of a personal God brings out marvelously the grandeur of man made in his image, of man as person. From this follows that other characteristic which sets man apart from all visible creatures: to act as a man, to act freely, to be responsible, is to answer for oneself and one's acts before God. The majesty of the Questioner reflects upon the one called to account and in some way reveals him to himself. Finally, man is loved, saved, and redeemed by the death of the only Son of God, and destined by pure grace to enter into the threefold life.

We may then ask the following question: if it is true that man is in danger of abusing goods, of becoming a slave to them instead of using them to conquer a higher liberty, is it not better to teach him to do without things rather than to make things which will enslave him tomorrow?

That, we know, is the solution chosen by oriental wisdom. A Christian who has heard the word of the gospel, "What will it profit a man, if he gains the whole world and forfeits his life?" (Matt. 16:26), will not find the language of the Philosophers of the Celestial Way foreign to him. He knows that, apart from the metaphysical context, they touch a truth that the Christian faith is not going to blunt, but raise to quite supernatural power. He knows that every man will experience once in his lifetime the moment when he is really called to leave practically everything, and to leave himself, to enter the Kingdom and share in perfect freedom. This hour of truth, every Christian knows, is not only decisive, but may strike from one minute to the next.

It is really an hour of truth, for the whole person is at stake, and illusions and evasions are equally impossible. The riches of art and technology are left a long way behind, at the far end of the shore that he is about to leave. Psychological techniques themselves have become equally ridiculous. Man is as helpless as the day he was born, with no other resource outside himself than the infinite mercy, and none within himself but the burning flame of charity, the gift of God, which it was his vocation to preserve and increase. The achievement of culture could not be authentically human if by some means or other it did not take this into account; if the liberation which it is considered to give did not help this interior disposability which will not tolerate compromise.

Yet Christian wisdom, which we see is even more exacting than oriental wisdom, has taken a very different attitude to the problem of methods in general and of technical achievement in particular. It does not deny the prime importance of contemplation. On the contrary, it affirms it with incomparable force, but it differs most sharply from oriental thought, and it is there that it finds its own solutions to this problem of the end and the means.

CHRISTIAN CONTEMPLATION

Christian contemplation emanates from the love of charity, which plays the role of beginning and end, and which is also the means of attaining the highest wisdom. When, in the soul emptied of itself, the Spirit which has diffused the divine agape in our hearts takes the initiative of love into its hands, the soul, says spiritual tradition, is moved more than it moves, and love, whose essential function is to realize union, unites God and the soul in such a way that the latter in some way gains experience of the hidden mystery of its God. It knows him in a new way, not by a discursive knowledge, however elevated, but through this non-conceptual knowledge which springs out of love itself. St. Thomas Aquinas, who knew these two wisdoms, did not hesitate to describe theology as straw, by comparison with this superior knowledge of the gifts of the Holy Spirit. This gives real meaning to the words of the apostle: "He who is united to the Lord becomes one spirit with him" (I Cor. 6:17).

Because contemplation is the operation of the love of charity, it will not be in opposition to action but will stimulate it. Charity in relation to God implies this fusion which St. Augustine described thus: *"Idem velle, idem nolle."* First it is assent to what God is in himself beyond all created things, joy that God should be God. One of the most beautiful and lofty expressions of love I find in this quotation from a French spiritual writer of the seventeenth century: "My God, I thank you for what you are in yourself, as much as for the greatest grace that I have and ever can have." But love wants what God wants; not only that "thy name be hallowed"—but also that "thy kingdom come," that "thy will be done, on earth as it is in heaven." And this fusion of the will of man and the will of God implies that man in his place and in his own vocation works for the coming of the Kingdom and the accomplish-

ment of the divine will. Action proceeds from the con-
templative love.

From the primacy of contemplation follows, in a Christian perspective, not the condemnation, but the benedic-
tion of every human effort which seeks to perfect man in
accordance with his natural and supernatural capacities.
Charity has in itself enough resources to bring all things
back to God in Christ. "All are yours," said the apostle,
"and you are Christ's, and Christ is God's" (I Cor. 3:22-23),
and, in the same epistle to the Corinthians: "Whether you
eat or drink, or whatever you do, do all to the glory of
God" (I Cor. 10:31).

THE ANSWER TO THE PARADOX

We can now try, in the light of revelation, to answer
our question, whether we should not do better to teach
man to do without rather than to use created goods, if the
risk of abuse is so great.

The gospel does not contradict Genesis. The sayings,
"What will it profit a man, if he gain the whole world and
forfeits his life?" and "Leave the dead to bury their dead,"
are not in antithesis to the primitive command to man to
subdue the earth, and to develop himself according to his
full nature.

The answer to the paradox seems to us to be found in
the Catholic doctrine of "evangelical counsels" and in their
right application. I borrow from a Carthusian monk a formulation of this doctrine which seems particularly felici-
tous in its brevity:

"The theologian will first say that the *counsel* of poverty, the invitation to free oneself from things, especially
from things that it is natural for man to want and to possess in moderation, can only be followed in response to the

call of grace, which affects souls in different ways and each one in its own time. We all need to withdraw and to attend to interior witness, but this light which detaches us radically and finally liberates us from the tangible must be given us by God as a gift, for which our generosity and our patience must prepare us, a lengthy process for some, in a life whose engagements and servitudes may be part of our spiritual destiny. For lack of these distinctions, this preparation and this filial docility, ascesis, and meditation can also mislead souls; they offer precisely the danger . . . of a technique!

"The second remark of the Christian moralist is the following: to free ourselves of possessions is wisdom for all of us, when God calls us to do so, but to free others, or even to invite them to free themselves, is no virtue whatever. Poverty and obedience help the spiritual progress of individuals; abundance and liberty are good things which we should guarantee to every civil society as far as we are able. An ascetic may well renounce human remedies, if he receives from God this virtue; but the Russian peasants who as late as the nineteenth century let smallpox carry off their children or strike them with blindness because vaccination was a diabolical way of escaping the will of God, and because blindness was a help rather than a hindrance to salvation, seem to us to be very far removed from the spirit of the Christian west; though their simplicity may be touching, we should be guilty if we were to imitate them." [4]

What then is the theological significance of this position in relation to our problem?

I see it on two planes:

1. *On the individual plane.* Catholicism recognizes that

[4] "Valeur humaine de la technique," in *Nova et Vetera* (Fribourg, 1950), I, 12-13.

the effective practice of the evangelical counsels—which corresponds here to the minimum use of human means or wealth—is one of the ways that certain baptized Christians are called to take, by a special vocation from our Lord. They even call this way "the way of perfection," in opposition to "the common way." That does not mean that those who set out upon it are more perfect than those who follow another way, common to the majority of Christians, towards the same perfection, but that the Christian takes this way as being more likely to lead to the perfection of love: "If you would be perfect, go, sell what you possess . . . and come, follow me" (Matt. 19:21). We shall see that every Christian must be ready to accomplish, when faithfulness to Christ requires it, acts of the greatest renunciation. But to some Christ *counsels* that they should choose them even when there is no compulsion.

However many Christians are called to follow this way, it will never be more than a tiny minority. God will ask them, it is true, to serve chiefly the Kingdom and to renounce a human vocation. If they are technicians, artists, or scientists, that is accidental. Their role among humanity is to remind us of the Kingdom's absolutes. But what might appear to be a withdrawal from the world's stage, these Christians, so long as they are faithful to their vocation, render distinguished service to the world and culture in addition. What art and pure and disinterested learning bring to culture, but from the very heart of culture, by their very "uselessness" and gratuitousness, all this is brought eminently and as though from a transcendent source by life lived according to the evangelical counsels. A civilization which had no place for this life would stifle the breath of art and pure knowledge within itself, and would soon lose all title to the name of civilization.

But the doctrine of the evangelical counsels applies not only to those of whom we have just been speaking. Every baptized Christian may be called to live this same renunciation in a similar spirit, that is, through love of Christ, if the circumstances of his life, which in themselves express a divine will and thus a vocation, compel him. How many have accepted the deprivations of poverty and chastity as a way of being true to their faith, or simply to a divine precept, who would have thought it presumptuous to choose them?

Yet these Christians retain a specifically human vocation: they are scientists, technicians, artists. The call to enter into the Kingdom does not for them entail renunciation of these tasks of building the terrestrial city. On the contrary, as has been said, they are invited to work in it with all the greater earnestness and generosity because, through their faith, they understand the dignity hidden in each of their human brothers, believing or unbelieving.

They have grace to live fully the spirit of the gospel— this constant readiness to be of service of which we spoke earlier—if they are faithful, without any diminution of their passionate interest in their human labor. This is the grace which belongs to their state, the special hold which theological charity has on their life. In this way they will follow St. Paul's advice: "The appointed time has grown very short; from now on . . . let those who deal with the world [live] as though they had no dealings with it" (I Cor. 7:29-31), that is, without being enslaved to it, with the freedom which allows you to take everything without being possessed by anything except by God.

2. *On the social plane.* The evangelical counsels, the maxims of the Sermon on the Mount, envisage access to the Kingdom of God and the demands of life in harmony with

this Kingdom. Now it is individual people and not states or societies which are called to enter this Kingdom. To apply to temporal society as such the counsels of the gospel is not only a mistake but is ultimately to imperil the spiritual life of the majority of this society; the consequence is often to fall short of the demands of love and justice. To try to make these maxims into principles of social justice, is to build a society dominated by injustice. It would amount, for example, to condemning the right to strike, or of lawful defense. It would be to confuse trust in Providence with culpable improvidence, the source of want and famine for the poorest members of the community (the rich will always find a way out!). God's plan for the city is not that.

The counsel of detachment may be followed by individuals, and should be, where it applies to their own spirit, but society as such is subject to other laws. All the work of the technician and the scientist, as of all who serve the temporal community, contributes toward another objective, which although it is not explicitly defined in the New Testament, is no less in accord with what revelation teaches us about God's designs for man and his double vocation. If it is truly lived by Christians, the evangelical spirit will reflect upon the life of the city. You would misunderstand me if you were to interpret my thought as being that the gospel has no word for the temporal order. In fact, the temporal order cannot do without the evangelical leaven of the gospel.

On the personal plane, the evangelist's message retains its full force: "If your right eye causes you to sin, pluck it out and throw it away: it is better that you lose one of your members than that your whole body be thrown into hell"

(Matt. 5:29). On that level, better to lose everything than seriously to imperil the precious pearl of charity.

On the plane of society, our answer to our question should be no: the Christian must face the real risks which technology causes him to run. On that plane, it seems possible to say: every risk must be taken except that of mutilating man. The renunciation of real progress in man's mastery of the world would be that risk.

SCOTT I. PARADISE

Christian Mission and the Technician Mentality in America

TECHNOLOGY and industry are creating, it is generally con-
ceded, a universal culture. And while Europeans are justly
proud of their great scientists, and their theologians have
given profound thought to the relationship of theology to
technology (witness the foregoing essays), they gladly admit that the United States is the land of technicians. Here
the joining of applied science and industry has been so
intimate that the two have become one flesh and given
birth to the world's most highly developed technological
civilization. In this marriage industry has been the dominant partner. Its economic rationale has supplied its direction and drive, and its principles of social organization
have given it shape. Technology has been the junior partner, even the willing servant of industry. But so well has
it served that it has given industry an almost explosive
dynamic and colored the whole industrial climate of
opinion with the technician mentality.

THE TECHNICIAN MENTALITY IN AMERICA

American industrial culture is also, then, a technological
culture, and the power of industry has permeated almost
every nook and cranny of American society with technological values, attitudes, and ways of thought. And although
many still flourish whose minds in part resist capture by

the technician mentality, they are not generally regarded as either characteristic or influential Americans today. Hence most of the attributes described in the foregoing essays as belonging to technicians tend to be true of Americans also, but to an exaggerated degree.

Random illustrations might include first of all the observation that in America the progressionist spirit referred to by Ladrière has become for a mobile people with neither social stabilities nor much reverence for the past a kind of national fetish. We do not look on permanence as being the normal state of affairs that is occasionally disrupted by change. For us not to change is to stagnate. And change is our confirmed habit, our only absolute, our way of life. So we like to live in new houses if not in new neighborhoods. Our cars are subjected to an annual model change. Innovation is the rule in our manufacturing processes as we pour out ever-increasing quantities of new products. Of course, this desire always to experience or possess some new thing is not new in human history but in technological society, especially in America, it has been prodigiously emphasized.

The same is true of the optimism of the technician mentality about which Ladrière also speaks. Not only is change normal and inevitable, but it is also good. To be *new* is to be *better*. And the problems accompanying some technological innovations can be dealt with by yet more technological innovation. It may be that the Englishman Francis Bacon first postulated human salvation in terms of technological advance, but it was the American Henry Ford who demonstrated the messiahship of technology in terms that caught the imagination of the whole world. Likewise, the technician's passion, also mentioned by Ladrière, to reduce everything to the state of a useful object is perhaps more characteristic of the American than the European. All things in the universe are for us to use, to manipulate, and bend to our purposes. That is their significance. And proud of our pragmatism, we honor our practical men and ridicule the eggheads.

The American mind-set, in its realistic, down-to-earth empiricism, reflects the technician mentality par excellence. Ladrière calls this "the nihilism of the technician" because it excludes consideration of questions of ultimate meaning and makes no reference to the transcendent. Related to this phenomenon, we have in America also signs of the disappearance of the sacred and the devaluation of the symbol, and both of these affect seriously our ability to think in religious terms.

The technician, however, defends this focus on the grounds that it is better to make progress by solving small manageable technical problems than to wallow endlessly with great metaphysical questions that can never be conclusively answered. And why worry about questions of ultimate meaning when significant meaning for life is found in bettering the human lot by successfully meeting immediate technical challenges in the here and now? "Leave it to the Europeans to argue and fret about questions of meaning and points of ideology. Let's get on with the job."

THE THEOLOGICAL PROBLEM
FOR CHRISTIAN FAITH

In Europe the challenge that the technician mentality makes to the churches stands out starkly. In the past hundred years, in almost every European country, the church has shown alarming decline in strength and membership.

And careful studies have shown that, generally speaking, the areas of greatest industrial technological development display the greatest ecclestiastical decline.[1] On the other hand, despite the deeper inroads the technician mentality has made on American thought and attitudes, our churches have been enjoying unprecedented prestige and popularity. In fact, the contrast between the experience of the European and American churches raises the questions, "Is the testimony of Ladrière, Russo, and the others correct?" "Perhaps their analysis of the technician mentality is mistaken. Does not the American experience indeed show that the technician mentality and traditional Christian faith are friends and not enemies?"

An examination of American Christianity should disabuse us of this hope. A European churchman, observing the booming life in American churches, is reported to have said, "It's splendid, but is it Christian?" And Will Herberg[2] and others have argued convincingly that social forces in American life having little to do with Christianity are primarily responsible for this growth in church membership. A plethora of books published since Herberg's have insistently claimed that, our full pews notwithstanding, all is not well with the Christian faith in America.[3] And if the judgment of scholars is not enough, the large numbers

[1] F. Boulard, *An Introduction to Religious Sociology*, (London: Darton, Longman & Todd Ltd.), 1960.
[2] Will Herberg, *Protestant, Catholic, Jew* (Garden City, New York: Doubleday & Company, Inc.), 1955.
[3] Viz. Peter Berger, *The Noise of Solemn Assemblies* (Garden City, New York: Doubleday & Company, Inc.), 1961; Martin Marty, *The New Shape of American Religion* (New York: Harper & Row, Publishers), 1959; Reinhold Niebuhr, *Pious and Secular America* (New York: Charles Scribner's Sons), 1958.

of educated and loyal churchmen who freely admit that they have little understanding of or interest in the Christian faith add a loud "amen" to the scholars' opinion. The least we can say is that there is reason to suspect that even though the institutional church still thrives, the technician mentality is nevertheless undermining its theological foundations.

The foregoing essays spell out, in a striking way, the incongruities between traditional Christianity and the contemporary form of the technician mentality and imply a conflict between the two approaches. But even more, in this country there appears another element of the technician mentality that is of fundamental importance. Christianity has tended to look to the past. A particular historical event that happened almost two thousand years ago stands as the focal point in history and the clue to all life. This event has been seen to have final and eternal significance. And through the Bible, tradition, faith, and mystical experience this truth can be appropriated. For the technician, however, all these are hopelessly unreliable means to grasp reality. Truth is approximated by means of the scientific method and by no other means. If scientific findings at certain points confirm the traditional insights of religion, "Why, good luck to religion." But apart from making religious people feel good it has no other significance. Sigmund Freud's position is characteristic of the technician on this point:

"We believe that it is possible for scientific work to discover something about the reality of the world through which we can increase our power and according to which we can regulate our life. If this belief is an illusion, then we are in the same position as you (the religious person), but science has shown us by numerous and significant successes that it is no illusion. . . . But it would be an illusion to suppose that we could get anywhere else what it cannot give us." [4]

In this country such a position is far more widely assumed and lived by than it is articulated or defended. But in any case it breeds, if not hostility, at least as profound an indifference to Christianity and theological questions as can be found in Europe.

Admittedly the manager, the technician, the engineer may at home say grace at meals, send his children to Sunday school, and perhaps even attend church himself. But when he is thinking about his work, economics, politics, that is, the important issues that confront him, serious religious concern is not very evident.

On its part, the leadership of the Church often returns the antipathy and indifference of the technician. Although inevitably affected by the technician mentality, the thinking of the large fundamentalist wing of the Church tries to continue as if the scientific technological industrial revolution had never taken place. This part of the Church wants to believe that the concepts, imagery, and even the words of prescientific society are just as plausible, meaningful, and true as they ever were. The Church then does not have to take the technician mentality into account, for insofar as it challenges the traditional Christian beliefs, the technician mentality is simply wrong. This kind of Christian seems to have woven an intellectual cocoon around himself that is impervious to the corroding acids

[4] *Future of an Illusion* (Doubleday & Company, 1957), pp. 99, 102.

of the technician's kind of thinking. This Christian can speak but he cannot listen. And above all, he will not be changed. While this attitude is found in its purest form in fundamentalist churches, most churches possess a certain measure of it. For the most part, however, church leadership seeks accommodation with the world of the technician. It seeks to compromise by staking out certain areas of life where the relevance of religion must be preserved, and handing over the rest of life to be guided by the technician's kind of thinking. Religion is concerned with the private relationships between people. Science and technology deal with the world of things. The Church is active in the private environment of the family, home, and residence. Science and technology dominate the area of work and the public sphere of politics and economics. As long as the technician respects this division of spheres of influence, religion and science do not need to conflict. And many clergy and devout laymen believe that this armistice can be permanent. But it has resulted in demanding of many laymen a schizoid manner of thought: they live their lives not on the basis of one overarching world view but rather on two world views. And this compromise has made it possible for the clergyman to stand behind his ecclesiastical iron curtain either assuming the Church has met the challenge of science and industry or else generally ignoring it. The Church's safety, however, is only apparent. The Christian and the scientific technological ways of thinking are unlikely to maintain a permanent compromise. The battle for men's minds goes on if not in pitched battles, at least by subversion. Though muted, a crisis exists. But it is not a crisis in which the technician mentality is threatened.

THE COMMUNICATION PROBLEM
FOR CHRISTIAN FAITH

Since the technician mentality seems likely to dominate the minds of men for the foreseeable future, those concerned with the future of the Christian faith must take this challenge to it seriously. This would certainly involve opening up serious discussions in which the technician mentality is examined from the point of view of the Christian faith and the Christian faith is examined from the point of view of the technician mentality. Such dialogue, if sustained, might reveal how Christian theology might be shaped so as to speak more intelligibly and convincingly to the technological age. At the same time the dialogue might result in the modification of the mentality of technicians so as to include within it some of the profoundest insights of the Christian faith. This is the hope for the future of Christianity and also the hope for the future of mankind.

This kind of dialogue, however, is confusing to try to describe. Part of the confusion springs from the likelihood of it taking place simultaneously on three levels. On one level the dialogue could take place between Christian laymen who are primarily committed to the technician's way of thinking and clergymen. At another level, or in other circumstances, the dialogue might take place between men who are partly committed to the Christian faith and partly to the technician's world view and other men who are given wholly to the technician's way of thinking. And within the mind of almost every Christian participating in the dialogue there will also occur an inner dialogue between the part of him committed to the Christian faith and the part of him influenced by the technician mentality. At all three of these levels dialogue must be attempted. In what follows then, I shall assume that individuals are the participants, and I shall refer to all three levels of the dialogue collectively as the dialogue between the Christian faith and the technician mentality.

In beginning the dialogue one real difficulty lies in the shape and location of the institutional church. In industrial society most men today live in two worlds: the world of home and residential neighborhood, on the one hand, and the world of work in the business community or industrial corporation, on the other. These two worlds are separate and distinct; a psychological chasm yawns between them even where a geographical one is absent. In one of these worlds one lives his private life. Here the institutional church is located. If the Christian faith makes sense, it is most likely to make sense here. Here also is the place of leisure, love, and the consumption of goods. In the other world where men spend most of their waking hours, one is economically productive and enters into the most blatant form of the struggle for survival. This world is the stronghold of the technician mentality, no form of the institutional church exists here, questions of ultimate meaning are excluded, and even the mention of the name of God seems inappropriate. Though in this country literally millions pass from one of these worlds to the other and back again every day, very little real dialogue takes place between the Christian faith and the technician mentality.

In order to begin the dialogue, the three opening gambits most Christian laymen often make when they enter the world of business and industry fail equally. First, there are some who seriously accept the Christian categories of thought as their minister presents them and then unflinchingly repeat and apply them to their immediate industrial situation. In spite of some notable exceptions this approach is usually made in the lower echelons of industry; it is generally an unsohisticated attempt to relate faith to the work situation. For example, a worker will repeatedly inveigh against swearing and Sunday overtime on the basis of the Third and Fourth Commandments, and tell his workmates they must be "twice born" to be saved. In cases like this the Christian worker is usually more interested in preaching to his fellows than in entering into dialogue with them.

Second, there are those who may take their faith just as seriously as the first sort of Christian but who lack the determination to take it with them out of the Church, home, or realm of private, personal relationships into the world of work. While they may try to follow the golden rule and be decent and kind at their work, they nevertheless adopt the technician mentality almost entirely in their work context. They may do this quite unconsciously because it seems natural and right to accept the compromise mentioned earlier. They may do it because they can see no viable way of translating the ideas they accept in the context of the Church into a form that makes any appropriate sense in the context of work. Whatever the motive, these Christians change their habits of thought with their hats and never enter into the kind of dialogue with their fellow workers that is needed.

Finally, there is the third and, by far, the most common type of Christian. These really have no other orientation except that offered them by the technician mentality. Just as those belonging to the first type find their thinking out of joint in the world of work, these find the thinking of the Church strange and uncongenial. Of course, they claim church membership and even hold office in the congregation, but they honestly admit they have only the vaguest notion of what Christianity is all about and are really without any serious religious interest. Theology not only seems dull and unintelligible, but it makes them uneasy as well. They expect the clergyman to understand those matters, but they themselves never expect to. Their ears are deaf to the Christian faith as it is traditionally interpreted. It just does not ring a bell.

Thus, through none of these three major types of Christian is any real dialogue between the Christian faith and the technician mentality opening up. This is the communication problem of the Church. This is part of the crisis for the Christian faith. This is the missionary challenge for our time.

METHODS FOR MISSION IN A TECHNOLOGICAL AGE

Nevertheless, in spite of the difficulties, on-going dialogue must begin. Indeed, it has already begun in some of the lay centers, evangelical academies, and industrial missions in Europe. However, in America in spite of—or, perhaps, because of—the Church's institutional strength dialogue is beginning in a much more modest way. The writer's experience has been with the Detroit Industrial Mission, which for six years has been working to initiate the kind of dialogue we have been describing. Most of the time these efforts have taken the form of an informal series of group discussions either in offices, conference rooms, or on the plant floor of factories, or else in restaurants, union halls, or homes close to the area of industrial involvement of the participants. Managers, union officials, and workers have been mainly involved, but only rarely have the representatives of the different occupations participated in the same group. In most cases a layman working in industry has been the convener, and a minister, usually but not always the leader, provoker, or theological resource person in the discussion. Almost every group has been made up of men who are strongly influenced by the technological mentality and who differ greatly in theological convictions. In fact, the majority in some groups are admitted atheists or agnostics.

Though these beginnings have not yet had time to bear impressive theological fruit, they have suggested certain clues or ground rules about how this dialogue might take place. The five clues which follow do not claim to be solutions but only hints.

1. *Exploring the full meaning of dialogue.* To begin with, the preceding analysis of the present situation of course suggests that its subtlety and complexity bankrupts the traditional missionary techniques. No longer can we assume that the Christian faith is a clearly understood and understandable body of doctrine. Nor can we assume that it can be communicated to unbelievers by Christians leading exemplary lives and at the right moment speaking the Christian Word. Though the Christian must be convinced that his faith offers him great riches, he has to admit that he understands neither more than a glimmer of its meaning in the world of technology, nor the way by which he can communicate it there. In an age dominated by the technician mentality, even the theologically educated Christian must discover the meaning of his faith in terms of the concrete situation. The required dialogue of discovery demands of the Christian a stance of extreme modesty, honesty, and restraint. The dialogue must take place through repeated encounters in which the Chris-

tian's initial role is one of listening and trying to understand. While confronting the technician mentality he stands utterly without authority.

When he does speak he can only win assent by making sense. And many of his contributions to the dialogue will probably die the death of bewildered indifference or impatient rejection. Progress can be measured by single moments of contact between the two mentalities involved. Most important perhaps, both sorts of participants must possess a willingness to learn and be changed by the other in the dialogue. The habit of dogmatic arrogance of both needs softening. Hopefully, the Christian can take the first step by demonstrating his own openness. If through such dialogue Christianity can be interpreted so as to be true to itself and yet make sense in terms of technician mentality, this may result both in the Christian's discovering the full meaning of his faith for our day and also in the redirection of industrial society and the recovery of meaning for industrial life.

2. *The necessity for affirmation.* Since the industrial revolution, Christian writers and theologians have traditionally been either ignorant or critical of the new world of industry and technology growing up around them. They have tended to find it strange and uncongenial and fraught with injustices and evils. And they sensed that it was a challenge if not a threat to the whole religious enterprise as they knew it. Many working in industry have sensed this lack of knowledge or critical attitude, and it has bred in them a suspicion or indulgent disregard for the clerical thought regarding industrial life that often inhibits successful discussion. Dialogue can only take place when trust is earned by the theologically trained participants demonstrating that they appreciate the achievement and promise

of industry and technology for mankind. Criticism may come later, but at the beginning the man whose thought is mastered by the technician mentality must feel that those representing the Christian side of the dialogue have come over to where he is, stood in his shoes, and looked at the world through his eyes.

3. *The need for relevance.* Repeatedly the writers of the foregoing essays have observed that Christianity is not being challenged directly by the technician mentality so much as it is being disregarded as being uninteresting and irrelevant. This suggests that in dialogue between the Christian faith and technician mentality, Christianity must be shown to make a practical difference in the world of work. The pragmatist must be met on his own grounds. At every point the Christian contribution to the discussion must be tested by the question, "So what?" Sometimes the answer to the question would affirm current behavior and attitudes but give them new meaning. Other times it would involve criticism and suggest changes. But in either case it could not be detached from the practical issues facing industry. This requires the formulation of Christian insights in terms of extreme concreteness. But perhaps in our time only in this way can the faith come alive and commend itself as worthy of serious consideration in the world of technology.

4. *An anthropological approach.* To the technician mentality the notion of God means nothing. For a man to talk about God in the context of industry, he must wrench himself loose from the mode of thinking he feels is appropriate there and think in ways that make little sense and may cause great embarrassment. Even more, in the context of industry any notion of the transcendent or question of meaning is very difficult. Whether confronting the

technician mentality in others or in himself, the Christian must use these concepts with extreme caution. But if he cannot begin by talking about God, he can talk about man. Human nature, human needs, and human values mean something that the technician mentality in even its purest form can deal with. And if the discussion can be channeled to plumb the depth of the ethical questions and hard decisions to be made in the struggle to shape a society in which all men can develop to their maximum potential, then concerns of the Christian faith and the interests of the technician mentality have come within hailing distance.

5. *The importance of the context of hearing.* One thing is certain. The kind of dialogue needed is not going on in many places in the Church today. And all our experience indicates that, except in a few favorable situations, this dialogue is not likely to take place in the context of the local church in big metropolitan areas. The atmosphere, the layman's ingrained expectations, and the other preoccupations of the institution all militate against significant dialogue between the Christian and the technician mentality taking place there. Moreover, the geographical and psychological location of the local church is too far removed from the context of Christian obedience in the industrial world. (The gulf between these two worlds is so vast that even if some theological ideas make sense when heard in church, they cannot be easily translated into terms that make sense in one's place of work.) No, the dialogue must be taken outside of the context of the Church into a more neutral context and perhaps into the context of industry itself. And if men who are deeply touched by the technician mentality can discover how to interpret the Christian faith so that it makes significant sense in this context, they will have discovered how to communicate the faith

to the modern world. But the Church's present structure
is not set up to carry on this kind of dialogue. Laymen
working in the secular institutions of our country are generally unable to initiate it without help. Local clergymen
generally lack the time, confidence, or special knowledge
to help them. The Church needs to devise new instruments to stimulate and aid laymen in this encounter.
These instruments must be organized outside the parish
structure, on an ecumenical base, and staffed by full time
clergymen or laymen who are both theologically trained
and sensitive to the nature and thought of our economic
institutions.

Work with two of these new instruments of dialogue
has involved me in many hundreds of discussions in which
the Christian faith and technician mentality engaged each
other. The experience has left me with profoundly am-
bivalent feelings. On the one hand, the difficulties of such
dialogue are enormous. In spite of the friendliness, trust,
and human contact characteristic of many of the discussions, real communication between the two modes of
thought is still extremely elusive. The utmost modesty is
necessary in describing the results.

On the other hand, my experience has invested this task
with a sense of extreme urgency. The power that technology is putting into men's hands is matched only by
their lack of understanding of its meaning. In our new
society our old attitudes, assumptions, and theories are so
inadequate that they are dangerous. Vigorous and reflective
thinking is necessary on a large scale if we are to acquire
the new mind and new heart necessary for preserving human values, indeed for the survival of humanity itself. For
just as it is folly to try to repair electrical fixtures without

having any understanding of electricity, so it is perilous to play with the new forces and institutions we are building without an understanding of their meaning. But to try seriously to understand and relate to the technological world growing around us is exactly what the Church has not yet tried to do. I find myself hard put to think of one first rate theological mind in America who has dedicated his life to studying the meaning of technology, or of one theological book of any weight trying to interpret it. It should be sobering to us that the essays here that grapple with these profound theological questions were not written in America but in Europe. For us they should be an example, a challenge, a beginning.

Christians in a
Technological Era

EDITED BY HUGH C. WHITE, JR.

Introduction by Margaret Mead

One urgent question that any thoughtful
Christian must meet squarely today is that
of the relation of religious faith to technology. Where can clear lines be drawn
to show the ethical implications of our
new technological demands? What possible answers does the science of cybernetics
reveal? What does liberty, or liberation,
mean today?

A significant ecumenical effort to discuss
these difficult, probing questions was made
in the 1961 Consultation held at Louvain,
France, between the World Student Christian Federation and Pax Romana. Here five
outstanding European theologians and philosophers—Protestant and Roman Catholic—convened to explore these issues.
Christians in a Technological Era is the
fruit of their discussion, and contains the
text of their remarks.

In her Introduction Margaret Mead, the
distinguished anthropologist, leaves no